AMBROISE PARÉ

The Apologie and Treatise

Containing the Voyages made into Divers Places
with many of his writings upon Surgery

The Classics of Science

LABOR IMPROBVS OMNIA VINCIT ·
A · P · AN · ÆT · 45 · · B ·

AMBROISE PARÉ

ÆT. 45

Engraving attributed to Jean Le Royer 1561

THE APOLOGIE
AND TREATISE OF
AMBROISE PARÉ

CONTAINING THE VOYAGES MADE
INTO DIVERS PLACES

WITH MANY OF HIS WRITINGS UPON
SURGERY

Edited and with an introduction by
GEOFFREY KEYNES
M.D., F.R.C.S., F.R.C.O.G.

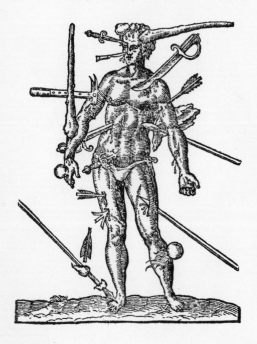

THE UNIVERSITY OF CHICAGO PRESS
CHICAGO ILLINOIS

THE UNIVERSITY OF CHICAGO PRESS
CHICAGO 37, ILLINOIS

W. J. Gage & Co., Limited, Toronto 2B, Canada
Falcon Educational Books, London, S.W. 1, England

CONTENTS

SELECTIONS FROM THE SURGICAL WRITINGS
(continued)

ILLUSTRATIONS

PORTRAITS OF AMBROISE PARÉ

1. AGE 45   *frontispiece*

Copper-plate engraving from the verso of the title-page of Paré's *Anatomie Universelle*, Paris, 1561, 8°. Signed with monogram LR, perhaps Jean Le Royer, engraver to the King.

2. AGE 65   *facing page* xviii

Wood engraving, unsigned, from the verso of the third leaf of Paré's *Œuvres*, Paris, 1575, f°.

3. AGE 68   *facing page* 3

Wood engraving, unsigned, from the verso of the fourth leaf of Paré's *Opéra*, Paris, 1582, f°.

4. AGE 72   *facing page* 91

Copper-plate engraving inserted in Paré's *Discours de la Mumie*, Paris, 1582, 4°. Signed: S.F., i.e. Stephanus Delaulne Fecit.

The Publishers are indebted to the following for permission to have photographs made of the portraits:

The Royal College of Physicians (no. 4)
The Royal College of Surgeons (no. 2)
The Hunterian Library, University of Glasgow (no. 1).

The "Wound Man" on the title-page is a reduced reproduction of the wood engraving on the title-page of the first English edition of *The Method of Curing Wounds made by Gun-shot*, London, 1617, 4°. The only extant copy is in the Bodleian Library, Oxford; the Publishers are indebted to Bodley's Librarian for a photograph.

The reproductions of woodcuts in the text are taken from Johnson's edition of Paré's *Works*, London, 1634, f°.

INTRODUCTION

THE history of surgery during the sixteenth century is dominated by the outstanding figure of one man, Ambroise Paré. He alone among the surgeons of Europe possessed those qualities which ensured pre-eminence, and, indeed, his survival as a Huguenot in Paris, during the turbulent years of his maturity—qualities which fitted him to be surgeon to four Kings of France and sometimes their counsellor as well, and enabled him at the same time to make important contributions to the practice of his profession. It has often been noticed that there is no more potent stimulus to advance in surgery than the exigencies of war, and the life of Paré illustrates this generalization in a striking manner, his practice in Paris being interrupted by service in the field during a series of campaigns in the wars waged by France both against external enemies and in civil conflict. Paré's powers of observation, common-sense reasoning, and deduction were exceptionally good, and his personality was strong enough for him to be able to maintain his innovations against the weight of tradition and the opposition of contemporary practitioners.

Surgery in sixteenth-century France was a despised profession and Paré did more than any other surgeon to raise its position to one of dignity and esteem. In Paris there were the three hierarchies of the Faculty of Physicians, the surgeons belonging to the College of St. Cosmas, or St. Côme, and the barber-surgeons.

It was the barber-surgeons who performed venesections and many of the operations of surgery, though they were despised by the members of the College of St. Côme. The physicians thought themselves vastly superior to both these bodies, presumably because they were more familiar with the classical languages and did not work with their hands. The members of the College of St. Côme were in the worst position, suffering from the oppressive superiority of the physicians and the successful competition of their inferiors, the barber-surgeons.

Paré was born in the year 1510, and so was the contemporary

of Bernard Palissy, the potter, who was actually born in the
same year; of the theologians Luther, Erasmus, Calvin, and
Knox; of the artists Raphael and Titian, and of the medical
reformers, Paracelsus and Vesalius. The *Fabrica* of Vesalius was
first published in 1543, when Paré was already laying the
foundation of his experience as a military surgeon, and it would
be tempting to assume that the new anatomy helped him to
advance, were it not that he had no Latin, and must perforce
have depended chiefly on his own observations and on those
older text-books which had been translated into French, such
as Guy de Chauliac and Jean de Vigo. Nevertheless, Paré must
have acquired some degree of familiarity with the work of
Vesalius. He frequently quotes the opinion of Vesalius in his
own anatomical writings, and his debt to Vesalius in his
anatomical illustrations is obvious—it was indeed acknow-
ledged by Paré in the preface to his *Anatomie Universelle*.

Paré was born in a village which has now been absorbed into
the city of Laval in the province of Maine. His father was
probably valet de chambre and barber to the Sieur de Laval,
and he may thus have acquired in his youth some interest in the
work of the barber-surgeons. His sister married one of these
who practised in Paris, and his elder brother Jean was also a
master barber-surgeon in Vitré. Little is known of his early life,
except that his education was certainly very meagre.

It is thought that he may have begun the study of surgery at
Vitré with his brother, who was a shrewd observer, being adept
at the exposure of beggars trying to benefit by counterfeit
disease. It is at any rate certain that Ambroise worked with a
barber-surgeon in the provinces before coming to Paris in 1532
or 1533. In Paris he started with no advantages, being appren-
ticed to a barber-surgeon, and having no Latin or Greek
without which he could not normally rise into the higher pro-
fessional grades. It was, however, this lowest grade that gave a
man of intelligence and originality the chance of making some
real advance in surgery. The surgeons of the College confined
themselves to the use of surface applications and minor surgery,
whereas the barber-surgeons, in addition to the practice of

venesection and cupping, performed many major operations. Some of them became 'specialists' in operations such as cutting for the stone, or the treatment of hernia. There were also those who operated for cataract, and others who treated fractures and dislocations. Many of these 'empirics' acquired great skill in their own operations, and inevitably came into conflict with the members of the Faculty and the surgeons' College, who were naturally jealous of their prowess. They were thus peripatetics, moving from one centre to another as their surroundings became too hot to hold them.

In these circumstances it was fortunate that Paré became a barber-surgeon with all the opportunities for observation and real surgical experience that this position offered. His apprenticeship, however, was brief. He was soon appointed a resident surgeon, or 'house-surgeon' as he would now be called, in the Hôtel-Dieu, an ancient monastic foundation which was still the only public hospital in Paris. Here he worked for three or four years, and it may be inferred from references in his later writings that he gained experience of the greatest importance to his future career.

Paré left the Hôtel-Dieu about 1536, but even then he did not take the examinations for admission to the ranks of the barber-surgeons, this being postponed until 1541. It was shortly after 1536 that he entered on his career as military surgeon.

It was not the custom in the sixteenth century to have doctors or surgeons appointed to the care of armies in the field. The medical practitioner, if there was one, was attached to the person of a general or noble leader, and so it came about that Paré, in his first campaign, was surgeon to the Mareschal de Montejan, colonel-general of the French infantry. It has been suggested that he took this position because at this time he could not afford the fees necessary for the examinations which would enable him legally to practise as a barber-surgeon in Paris. If this is true, the chance circumstance of Paré's poverty has served to benefit mankind by forcing this great man to turn his mind immediately to the treatment of gunshot wounds and the performance of amputations instead of the trivialities of routine practice, where his originality and powers of observation might not for many years have found an outlet. In the course of his first campaign he quickly realized that the accepted method of treating gunshot wounds with boiling oil did more harm than good. He substituted a more humane and less destructive dressing, and soon established a reputation for skill in the treatment of wounds, so that his services were in great demand. When his first employer, de Montejan, died during the campaign, the succeeding commander tried to keep Paré in his employ, but it may be supposed that by now the young surgeon had accumulated all the funds he needed. He therefore refused to stay with the army, and returned to Paris where he resumed the study of anatomy. He passed his examinations for admission to the community of barber-surgeons in 1541, and soon afterwards married Jeanne Mazelin, a woman of his own class, by whom he had three children. The first two died as infants and only the third, a daughter, survived to reach adult life.

Knowledge of Paré's first campaign, and indeed of all of them, is derived from his *Apology and Treatise containing the Voyages made into divers places*. The reprinting of this treatise in English is the main object of the present volume, since it contains what amounts to an autobiography covering fifty years of Paré's life from the age of twenty-six to seventy-five. The *Apology and Treatise* was first published in the fourth edition of Paré's collected works, 1585. It was written not long before this in answer to an attack by a physician, Étienne Gourmelen, in his book, *Chirurgicæ artis, ex Hippocratis & aliorum veterum medicorum decretis*, Libri III, Paris, 1580, in which he tried to prove that Paré's methods of treating wounds and his use of the ligature to control haemorrhage in amputations were bad practice. Even today it is often believed and stated that Paré invented the ligature of large arteries, though he himself made no claim to this. His only claim, as he makes clear in the *Apology*, was that he first applied, in performing amputations, a technique used by many of the ancients in other operations. Having embarked on this explanation, Paré takes the opportunity of illustrating his points by giving an account of all the campaigns in which he took a part, with many anecdotes of his own life and experiences throughout his most active years. We may be grateful to Paré for having thus provided us with an incomparable record of the practice of surgery, mainly military, in the sixteenth century, but he was not consciously acting as historian. His main object was to crush his opponent with the weight of his knowledge gained by direct observation and experience, and to point the contrast with Gourmelen's dependence on knowledge derived from books. Paré addresses Gourmelen scornfully throughout as *mon petit maître*, and has no difficulty in disposing of his arguments, but, although in his seventh decade, Paré is still so full of zest and aggressiveness that he lets his pen run on long after his enemy's defences have been demolished. The result is one of the most entertaining surgical treatises ever written. It is necessarily egotistical, and Paré was not one to mince his words or to suppress any lurid detail lest he should be accused of lack of refinement. His method was to describe things as he saw them, and it was his pleasure to draw attention to his own virtues in marginal notes which leave the reader in no doubt as to the qualities of the writer.

To give a detailed account of Paré's life from 1541 would largely be to recapitulate what the reader will find related in the *Apology and Treatise*. It is therefore only necessary now to provide a biographical scaffolding of outstanding events.

While living in Paris after his first campaign Paré began to acquire property both in the neighbourhood of his house in the parish of St. André des Arts on the left bank of the Seine, and at Meudon where he had a house and vineyard. Rabelais was curé of Meudon for a short time before his death in 1553, but may never have been there, and it is improbable that he and Paré were acquainted. There is however, a strong probability that Paré was a friend of Montaigne, though no direct evidence of their friendship can be found. They were both attached to the court of Henri III, and they record in their writings the same 'monsters', or abnormalities in human beings, which are likely to have caught their attention at the same time.

In the autumn of 1542 Paré journeyed with the Vicomte de Rohan to the siege of Perpignan, and it was here that he enhanced his reputation by removing an arquebus ball from the shoulder of Monsieur de Brissac, Grand Master of the Artillery. The injury had baffled de Brissac's surgeons, but Paré caused the patient to assume the exact position that he was in at the time of receiving the injury, and by this simple trick quickly located the ball. This campaign was soon over, and Paré returned to Paris. The principle of reconstructing the course of a projectile in the body by placing the parts in their position at the time of injury had already in 1539 been described by Paré to Sylvius (Jacques Dubois), professor of medicine at Paris and a famous, though unenlightened, anatomist, and Paré had been persuaded to put his views on paper. The result was his first book, *La Methode de Traicter les Playes Faictes par Harcquebutes et Aultres Bastons à Feu: et de Celles qui sont Faictes par Fleches, Dardz & Semblables: aussi des Combustions Specialement Faictes par le Pouldre à Canon*. This was published in 1545 and it will be noticed that Paré took the opportunity to add something about his unconventional views on the supposed poisoning of wounds by gunpowder.

His next journey, in 1543, was to Brittany to meet a threatened invasion by the English, again with the Vicomte de Rohan, but the attack was abandoned, and Paré soon returned home. In 1544 he was again with the army for a short time at Landrecy, but this brought him no new experience.

In 1545 Paré was at the siege of Boulogne, where the Duc de Guise suffered a terrible injury, a lance passing through his head from above the right eye to behind the left ear: Paré described the incident in the second edition of his first book (1552) but made no claim that he was professionally concerned in the treatment of the Duc. After his return to Paris, Paré turned his attention to the intensive study of anatomy, working in conjunction with his friend Thierry de Héry, another barber-surgeon, and published in 1549 his small treatise *Briefve collec-*

tion de l'administration Anatomique: avec la maniere de conjoindre les os. The most remarkable part of this was an appendix on obstetrics, in which Paré first described in print the use of podalic version. Evidently his practice had included some midwifery, and characteristically he soon made an original and important contribution to the subject.

Paré's interest in anatomy was very great, and had to be acquired, as already mentioned, without much help from Vesalius. He relates that at this period he obtained for his own use the body of a criminal and dissected the whole of one side, leaving the other side untouched. He claimed that he kept the body with all its organs in good condition for over twenty-seven years.[1]

In 1552 Paré accompanied his old employer, the Vicomte de Rohan, to Germany, where he gained new fame as 'the charitable surgeon' by taking the trouble to save the lives of common soldiers who would ordinarily have had their throats cut by their comrades to save them from a worse fate at the hands of the peasantry. It was on his way back from their campaign in 1552, at the siege of Danvillier, that Paré first used the ligature in amputating a leg. He did not publish a description of this innovation until 1564 in his *Dix Livres de la Chirurgie*, but in the meantime he had gained full confidence in the method by repeated trial, and advised complete abandonment of the use of the cautery, which he had advocated in 1552.

Paré's reputation as a military surgeon was by now widespread, and he was persuaded by Monsieur de Vendôme, afterwards King of Navarre, to accompany him on a campaign in Picardy. This led to his introduction to King Henri II, who appointed him one of his surgeons in ordinary, and so to his remarkable experiences at the siege of Metz, where he was smuggled through the lines of the Emperor Charles I to attend to the sick and wounded in the besieged city. Paré's description of this campaign surpasses all the others in interest, and it is plain to see why he was honoured and handsomely rewarded by the King on his return after the raising of the siege.

In 1550 Paré suffered capture by the Spaniards at Hesdin,

[1] *Œuvres*, ed. Malgaigne, vol. iii, p. 479.

where he had been sent by the King, and narrowly escaped with
his life. He would in fact have been killed had he not attached
himself in disguise to an important prisoner, Monsieur de
Martigues, who requested that he be allowed to accompany
him to dress his wounds. Paré knew, however, that de Martigues was bound to die and was relieved when he was ordered
to hand over the care of his patient to a Spanish mountebank
and impostor. He thus escaped the blame for de Martigue's
death, but was asked to embalm the body. This he did so
skilfully, giving meanwhile an impressive anatomical discourse,
that he was asked to enter the service of the Duke of Savoy.
Paré courageously refused, but afterwards gained his freedom
by curing the ulcerated leg of Monsieur de Vaudeville, and was
again rewarded by the King on his return.

By 1554 Paré's reputation and position were such that the
members of the College of St. Côme were anxious to count
him among their number. He was therefore hurried through
the formalities without any proper examination and without
being charged the usual fees. The College had undoubtedly
gained in standing and influence by enrolling so distinguished
a surgeon and so close a friend of the King.

For more than three years after this signal recognition of his
worth Paré worked at anatomy and surgery in Paris until in
1558 the King sent him to Doullens. The town was then being
besieged by the Spaniards, and Paré gained entry in disguise.

In the next year Henri II met his death by a head injury sustained by accident in a tourney. His successor, François II,
husband of Mary Queen of Scots, kept Paré attached to his
person, but survived for only eighteen months, dying in 1560.
Paré was again favoured by the next King, Charles IX, for
whom he demonstrated the uselessness of bezoar stone[1] as an
antidote to poison by means of a very horrible experiment on a
criminal. This is related in the section on bezoar stone in the
present selection (see p. 199).

The year 1561 was made memorable in Paré's life by three
events—the publication of two books, and the infliction of a

_____

[1] A concretion found in the intestines of ruminants, especially goats.

compound fracture of the leg by the kick of a horse. The books were *La Méthode Curative des Playes et Fractures de la Teste Humaine*, and the *Anatomie Universelle du Corps Humain*. The second of these is a very rare book, and of special interest because it contains a good portrait of Paré at the age of forty-five engraved on copper. This is reproduced here from the copy in the Hunterian Collection at the University of Glasgow, believed to be the only one in Great Britain.

In 1562 Paré had recovered from his injury, and was present at the sieges of Bourges and Rouen. At Rouen a high proportion of the wounded died from wound infection, among them Paré's friend, the King of Navarre, in spite of his having modified his dressing for gunshot wounds. He had favoured oil made from puppies, but now substituted a compound of honey and alum, and later another of turpentine and brandy.

In 1564 Paré published another important book, his *Dix Livres de la Chirurgie avec le Magasin des Instrumens necessaires à icelle*. This contains a second revision of his treatise on gunshot wounds with new sections on urology, and gives the first printed description of his use of the ligature in amputations, although he had already used it for many years. It was this innovation in particular which provoked the publication of Gourmelen's book and so resulted in the writing of the *Apology* for the *Œuvres* of 1585.

In the same year Paré accompanied the King and the Queen Regent on a political journey through France. It was on this tour and afterwards in Paris that he gained the extensive knowledge of the plague which enabled him to write his *Traicté de la Peste* published in 1568.

In 1567 Paré was again attending to the wounded in the civil war, but did not afterwards leave his work in Paris for more than short spells. He had now been for several years 'premier Chirurgeon du Roy', and tried by virtue of this office to bring all those who practised surgery in France under his control instead of under that of the premier barber-surgeon, but this aroused great opposition and the attempt was defeated.

Opinion has varied as to whether Paré was Catholic or

Protestant, but it seems to be certain that, although he con-
formed outwardly to Catholicism, his true sympathies were
with the Huguenots. His life may, therefore, have been in
danger at the Massacre of St. Bartholomew on 24 August 1572,
but he had friends in both camps, and he remained as far as
possible aloof from religious controversy while carrying on his
humane labours for the benefit of all—although he related in the
first edition of the *Œuvres* how an attempt was once made by
the Catholics to poison him at Rouen on account of his religion.

In the year of the massacre Paré published his *Cinq Livres de
Chirurgie*, consisting entirely of new material and forming one
of his most important contributions to surgical literature. It
deals chiefly with the science of fractures and dislocations and
gives the current teaching about bandages. Incidentally it contains the first description of fracture of the head of the femur.
Paré took the opportunity of replying in this book to the
virulent attack made by Julien Le Paulmier, a member of the
Faculty of Medicine, in his book *Traité de la Nature et Curation
des Playes de Pistolle, Harquebouses et Autres Bastons à Feu*, Caen,
1569. He ignored a second attack published in 1572. His *Deux
Livres de Chirurgie* appeared in 1573, again containing new
material though not strictly surgical, the subjects being chiefly
obstetrics and 'monsters' or teratology. In the second section
Paré betrays some belief in the efficacy of spells and in many
of the superstitions of his time, although he was active in the
exposure of other impostures, such as the virtues of the bezoar
stone, as already mentioned, and of mumia and unicorn's horn,
subjects dealt with in his *Discours de la Mumie, de la Licorne, des
Venins, et de la Peste*, 1582. In his section on 'monsters' Paré
recounts several instances of apparent change of sex, a subject
which also interested Montaigne and found a place in his *Essays*.

In November 1573 Paré's wife Jeanne Mazelin died at the
age of fifty-three. Three months later Paré married again, his
second wife being Jacqueline Rousselet, daughter of one of the
keepers of the King's stables. Paré was now aged sixty-four but
nevertheless had six children by his second wife. Two of these
were boys, but neither of them survived infancy, so that Paré,

AMBROISE PARÉ

ÆT. 65

Wood engraving 1575

in spite of two marriages and having numerous children, left no son to follow him.

In 1574 King Charles IX died of phthisis and Paré was set to perform the autopsy and embalmment of the body. Charles was succeeded by his brother, Henri III, who kept Paré in his service with the added title of *valet de chambre du roi*. In the next year, 1575, Paré published the first collected edition of his *Œuvres*. This was naturally written in French since the author had no Latin, and the Faculty of Physicians siezed on this opportunity to attack Paré as an ignorant charlatan. The attack was led by Étienne Gourmelen, the Dean of the Faculty, who called on an old enactment by which no medical work could be published without the permission of the Faculty. He was supported even by the Collège de St. Côme, although Paré was one of their Fellows. Paré published a brief reply to the charges of malpractice, and defended his use of the vernacular with the plea that even Hippocrates wrote in his own language, and that he himself wrote only to instruct young surgeons. The authorities duly reaffirmed the act cited by Gourmelen, but no action was taken to suppress Paré's book, which soon took its place as the most enlightened work on surgery ever published, placing the two sciences of medicine and surgery in their proper relationship and demonstrating the superiority of independent observation over blind acceptance of dogma. Thus Paré's life culminated in the production of a splendid surgical treatise as important in its sphere as the *Fabrica* of Vesalius published thirty years earlier—with the difference that the anatomist's book could be produced by a young man of twenty-eight, whereas the *Œuvres* of Paré could only be based on the experience and observations of a lifetime.

In the same year as Paré published this most important book he attended three lectures by a kindred spirit, Bernard Palissy, the subject being 'des fontaines, pierres, métaux et autres natures'.[1] It is said that no more is known of the intercourse between these two great men. Their lives ran on parallel lines,

---

[1] See *The Life of Bernard Palissy*, by Henry Morley, London, 1852, vol. ii, pp. 89–92.

both being originators and reformers. They were born and died within a few months of each other, though Palissy was at the end the less fortunate of the two, being imprisoned for his beliefs—the same as Paré's—in the Bastille, where he died in 1589.

Three more editions of the *Œuvres* were published in Paré's lifetime, the fourth edition of 1585 being the first to contain the *Apologie et Traité*. The first translation into Latin, reckoned as the third edition of the *Œuvres*, appeared in 1582; translations into Dutch and German were published, after Paré's death, in 1592 and 1601.

In August 1589 the King, Henri III, was fatally stabbed by a monk, but this happened at St. Cloud when Paré was not in attendance on his master. After the King's death the citizens of Paris rebelled against his successor, the King of Navarre, and in 1590 the city was besieged, being finally reduced by famine. This led to scenes of great horror, in the midst of which Paré came for the last time upon the stage of history. The Commander of the City, the Archbishop of Lyons, was answering the cries of the starving populace for surrender by deeds of greater cruelty, when Paré, now an old man living in retirement, confronted him in the street and in tempered words counselled him to give the people the peace they demanded. Paré's prestige was still so great that the Archbishop listened in silence and confessed afterwards that he had been awakened by his words. Paré died soon afterwards, on 20 December 1590, aged eighty, and was buried in the Church of St. André des Arts.

Paré's contribution to surgery is usually summarized by mentioning his three important 'discoveries'—the harmfulness of treating gunshot wounds with boiling oil, the use of the ligature in amputation, and podalic version in obstetrics—but in reality his contribution was far greater than this. He was in fact, by virtue of his personality and his independent mind, the emancipator of surgery from the dead hand of dogma. There was no comparable practitioner, during his time, in England or in any other country, and his influence was felt in every part of Europe. He left in his collected *Works* a monument to his own skill and humanity which is unsurpassed in the history of surgery, and this should always be available in some form for the perusal of his successors. In recent times there have been three excellent selections from Paré's works, in English, all of them concerned mainly with the presentation of the *Apologie et Traité*, edited by Stephen Paget (New York and London, 1897), by Francis R. Packard (New York and London, 1922), and by Dorothea Waley Singer (London, 1924). All these have been long out of print, so that for many years no part of Paré's work has been readily available. Paget added to the *Treatise containing the Voyages made into Divers Places* Paré's *Account of the Plague*. Packard printed only the *Apology and Treatise*, but provided a new translation from the original French. Mrs. Singer added to the *Apology and Treatise* the *Discourses on Gunshot Wounds* and the *Surgical Aphorisms and Rules*. The present edition seeks to extend the available material by adding to the *Apology and Treatise* a variety of Paré's writings to illustrate several kinds of surgery as practised in the sixteenth century, as well as Paré's independence of mind and character, though in some of these accounts Paré was no doubt describing operations as practised by others besides himself.

The reprint of the *Apology and Treatise* is accordingly followed by general remarks on the nature of surgery and surgical operations, and then by discourses on aneurysm, on hernia, on wounds in general and gunshot wounds in particular (including Paré's original views on their treatment), on mumia (being an exposure of its uselessness), on amputations (including the use of the ligature), on fractures in general and their treatment, on dislocations and their treatment, on cataract and the operation of couching, on cutting for the stone, on bezoar stones and the experiment to prove their uselessness as an antidote to poisons, and finally on *How to make Reports*, this being an important contribution on the technique of making postmortem examinations. No place has been found for other long sections of Paré's writings, such as his discourse *On Lues Venerea*, *On Tumours contrary to Nature*, on *Gout*, on *The Generation of Man* (including obstetrics), on *The Plague*, on

Poisons, on *Simple Medicines*, and on *Monsters and Prodigies*. Some of these omissions are greatly to be regretted, but it is believed that the passages reprinted represent Paré's work more fully than does any previous selection.

The source of the text here printed is the well-known folio printed by *Th. Cotes and R. Young, Anno. 1634.* This is stated on the title-page to be *translated out of Latine and compared with the French by Th. Johnson.* The identity of Thomas Johnson has not been established with absolute certainty, though there seems to be little doubt that he was the apothecary and botanist who was responsible for the revised edition of Gerard's *Herball* published in 1633.[1] It has been regretted by Miss Doe[2] and others that Johnson should have used the Latin edition of 1582, since this has many imperfections which are perpetuated in the English translation. Johnson sought to disarm his public by saying that his text was *compared with the French*, but his standard of scholarship was unequal to the task. Fortunately, however, the most important part of this reprint, *The Apology and Treatise*, was not translated by Johnson from the Latin, since it had not been printed in 1582, but was first published in the fourth edition of the *Œuvres*, 1585. Neither does Johnson claim to have translated it, stating that it was 'done out of French by George Baker, Surgeon of this City'. It is even possible that Johnson was only completing the translation of the rest, the task having been begun by Baker some years earlier. The book was indeed registered on 28 September 1629 as 'translated by Georg Baker'. Mrs. Singer, in printing her text from the edition of 1634, supplied many corrections of the spelling of names and other details, though she made some quite unnecessary omissions. In the present edition Johnson's spelling has been in the main preserved, some corrections being made without comment where it was thought necessary. The dates of Paré's journeys have also sometimes been corrected in accordance with Packard.

GEOFFREY KEYNES

[1] The question is discussed at length in Doe's *Bibliography*, pp. 172–81.
[2] Ibid., p. 170.

BIBLIOGRAPHY

THE following books are among those which have the most direct relation to the study of Paré's life and works:

MALGAIGNE, J. F.: *Œuvres Complètes d'Ambroise Paré revues et collationnées sur toutes les éditions, avec les variantes* . . . *precédées d'une Introduction sur l'origine et les progrès de la chirurgie en occident du sixième au seizième siècle, et sur la vie et les ouvrages d'Ambroise Paré.* Paris, Londres, 1840–1. 3 vols.

These volumes edited by Malgaigne (1806–65) are by far the most important source of information about Paré that we possess. An account of Malgaigne, himself a surgeon of note, will be found in Doe's *Bibliography of Paré*, pp. 144–52.

LE PAULMIER, Stéphan: *Ambroise Paré d'après de nouveaux documents.* Paris, 1884.

The author, a descendant of Julien Le Paulmier (see p. xviii), threw much interesting light on Paré's life by his researches.

PAGET, Stephen: *Ambroise Paré and His Times.* New York and London, 1897.

PACKARD, Francis R.: *Life and Times of Ambroise Paré with a New Translation of his Apology and an Account of his Journeys in Divers Places.* New York, London, 1922.

SINGER, Dorothea Waley: *Selections from the Works of Ambroise Paré with short Biography and Explanatory and Bibliographical Notes.* London, 1924.

DOE, Janet: *A Bibliography of the Works of Ambroise Paré.* Chicago, 1937.

The present editor is deeply indebted to the last four works in this list. They all contain full lists of references for the student.

PART ONE

ANNO ÆTATIS.
68

AMBROISE PARÉ

ÆT. 68

Wood engraving 1582

THE APOLOGIE
AND TREATISE, CONTAINING
THE VOYAGES MADE INTO
DIVERS PLACES
BY
Ambroise Paré of *Laval* in *Maine*, Counsellor
and cheefe Chirurgion to the King.

RUELY I had not put my hand to the penne, to
write on such a thing, were it not that some have
impudently injured, taxed, and more through
particular hatred, disgraced me, than for zeale or
love they beare to the publicke good; which was, concerning my manner of tying the Veines and Arteries, writing
thus as followeth.

*Malè igitur & nimiùm arroganter inconsultus & temerarius quid-
am, vasorum ustionem post emortui membri resectionem a veteribus
omnibus plurimùm commendatam & semper probatam damnare
ausus est, novum quendam deligandi vasa modum, contra veteres
omnes medicos sine ratione, experientia & judicio docere cupiens,
nec animadvertit majora multo pericula ex ipsa vasorum deliga-
tione quam acu partem sanam profunde transfigendo administrari
vult, imminere quàm ex ipsa ustione. Nam si acu nervosam
aliquam partem, vel nervum ipsum pupugerit, dum ita novo &
inusitato modo venam absurde conatur constringere, nova in-
flammatio necessariò consequetur, a qua Convulsio & a con-
vulsione cita mors. Quorum symptematum metu Galenus non*

ante transversa vulnera suere audebat (quod tamen minus erat periculosum) quàm musculorum aponeuroses denudasset. Adde quòd forcipes quibus post sectionem iterum carnem dilacerat, cum retracta versus originem vasa se posse extrahere somniat, non minorem adferant dolorem quàm ignita ferramenta admota. Quod si quis laniatum expertus incolumis evaserit, is Deo optimo maximo cuius Beneficentia crudelitate ista & carnificina liberatus est, maximas gratias habere & semper agere debet; which is thus: Ill then, and too arrogantly a certaine indiscreet and rash person would blame and condemne the cauterizing of vessells after the amputation of a rotten and corrupted member, much praised and commended and alwayes approved by the Ancients; desiring to shew and teach us without reason, judgement, and experience, a new way to tye the vessells, against the opinion of the Ancient Physitions, taking no heede, nor being well advised, that there happens farre greater perills, and accidents, through this new way of tying the vessells (which will have to be made with a needle, piercing deepely the sound part) than by the burning and ustion of the sayd vessells; for if the needle shall pricke any nervous part, yea the nerve it selfe, when he shall by this new and unaccustomed way absurdly constraine the veine by binding it, there must necessarily follow a new inflammation; from an inflammation a convulsion, from a convulsion death: for feare of which accidents, *Galen* never durst stitch transversall wounds, (which notwithstanding were lesse dangerous) before he had discovered the Aponeuroses of the muscles. Moreover the pincers with which after the section, the flesh is again dilacerated, while he thinkes to draw the vessells out which are drawne in toward their originall, bring no lesse paine than the cautering irons doe. And if any one having experimented this new manner of cruelty have escaped danger, he ought to render thankes to almighty God forever, through whose goodnesse he hath beene freed from such tyrannie, feeling rather his executioner than his methodicall Chirurgion.

O what sweete words are heere for one, who is sayd to be a wise and learned Doctor? he remembers not that his white beard admonisheth him, not to speake any thing unworthy of his age, and that he ought to put off and drive out of him all envie and rancor conceived against his neighbour. So now I will proove by authority, reason and experience, that the sayd Veines and Arteryes ought to be tyed.

The Authors answere.

Authorities.

As for Authorities, I will come to that of that worthy man *Hippocrates*, who wils and commands the cure of Fistula's in the fundament by ligature, as well to consume the callosity, as to avoyd hemorragie.

In the booke of Fistulaes of the fundament.

Galen in his method, speaking of a fluxe of blood made by an outward cause, of whom see heere the words, It is (saith he) most sure to tye the roote of the vessell, which I understand to be that which is most neere to the Liver, or the heart.

In the 3 chap., 5 book.

Avicen commands to tye the veine and the Arterie, after it is discovered, towards his originall.

Booke 4, leafe 4, 2 Treatise, chap. 17.

Guido of *Chauliac*, speaking of the wounds of the Veines and Arteries, injoyneth the Chirurgion to make the ligature in the vessell.

Treatise 3, doct. 1, chap. 3.

Master *Hollier* speaking of a fluxe of blood, commands expressely, to tye the vessells.

In the 3 book, chap. 5, of the matter of Chirurgery.

Calmetheus[1] in the chapter of the wounds in the Veines and Arteries, tells a most sure way to stay a fluxe of blood, by ligature of the vessell.

Wounds chap. 12.

Celsus from whom the sayd Physition hath snatched the most part of his booke, chargeth expressely, to tye the vessells in a fluxe of blood happening to wounds, as a remedy most easie and most sure.

In the 26 chap. of the 5 book.

Vesalius in his Chirurgery, willeth that the vessells be tyed in a fluxe of blood.

In the 4 ch. of the 3 booke.

---

[1] Antoine Chaumette, author of *Encheiridion Surgicum*, 1560, reissued as *Livre Portatif pour les Chirurgiens*, 1571.

In the book
1 treatise.

John de Vigo treating of a hemorragie in bleeding wounds, commands to tye the Veine, and the Artery.

In the 12.
chap. of the
2. booke.

Tagaultius treating of the meanes to stay a fluxe of blood, commands to pinch the Veine or Artery with a Crow or Parrot's bill, then to tye it with a very strong thred.

In the 4 treat.
11 chap., 1.
booke.

Peter of *Argillata* of *Bullogne*, discoursing of a fluxe of blood, and the meanes to stoppe it, giveth a fourth way expressely, which is made by ligature of the vessells.

In the first
booke 1 sec-
tion 1, chap.
16, page 5.
Upon the 88.
ch. of the
booke of
Paul.

John Andreas a Cruce, a *Venetian,* makes mention of a method, to stay a fluxe of blood by the ligature of the vessells.

D'Alechamps commands to tye the Veines, and Arteries.

See then (my little good man) the authorities which command you to tye the vessells. As for the reasons, I will debate of them.

In the book
2. ch. of
Angealogie,
leafe 76.

The hemorragie (say you) is not so much to be feared in the section of the Call,[1] as in that of the Varices, and the incision of the temporall Arteries, as after the amputation of a member. Now you your selfe command, that in cutting the Varices, the fluxe of blood be stopped by the ligature of the vessells. You command the same, speaking of the stitch,

In the booke
1, ch. of
stiches.

with the amputation and section of the Call, changed by the outward ayre, see heere your owne words: After that must bee considered concerning the Call: for if there be any part corrupted, putrified, withered, or blackish: First having tyed, for feare of a fluxe of blood, you doe not bid afterward to have it cauterized, but to say the truth, you have your eyes shut, and all your senses dulled, when you would speake against so sure a method, and that it is not but through anger, and an ill will. For there is nothing which hath more power to drive reason from her seate, than choler and anger. Moreover when one comes to cauterize the dismembred parts, oftentimes when the eschar comes to fall off, there happens a new flux of blood: As I have seene divers times, not having yet been inspired by God, with so sure a meanes then, when I used the heate of

[1] i.e. the omentum.

fire. Which if you have not found, or understood this method in the bookes of the Ancients, you ought not thus to tread it under your feete, and speake unluckely of one who all his life hath preferred the profit of the Common-wealth before his owne particular. Is it not more than reasonable to bee founded upon the saying of *Hippocrates*; upon whose authority you serve your selfe, which is thus? That what the medicament cureth not, the iron doth, and what the iron doth not amend, the fire exterminateth: It is a thing which savours not of a Christian, to fall to burning at the first dash without staying for any more gentle remedies. As you your selfe write, speaking of the condi-tions required in a Chirurgion to cure well; which passage you borrow from some other place: for that which may bee done gently without fire, is much more commended than otherwise. Is it not a thing which all schooles hold as a Maxime, that we must alwaies begin with most easie reme-dies, which if they be not sufficient, we must then come to extreame, following the doctrine of *Hippocrates*? *Galen* commands in the place before alledged, to treate or dresse the diseased quickly, safely, and with the least of paine that is possible.

In the chap-ter of burn-ing, 2 booke, leafe 266.

In the first booke, leafe the 5.

Galen in 4. booke of the Meth. and in the booke of Art of Hip-pocrates, Apho. the 6, booke 1. In the booke of Arte parva.

Let us come now to Reason.

Now so it is, that one cannot apply hot irons but with extreame and vehement paine in a sensible part, void of a Gangreene, which would be cause of a Convulsion, Feaver, yea oft times of death. Moreover, it would bee a long while afterwards before the poore patients were cured, because that by the action of the fire there is made an eschar, which proceeds from the subject flesh, which being fallen, nature must regenerate a new flesh in stead of that which hath beene burned, as also the bone remaines discovered and bare; and by this meanes, for the most part there remaines an Ulcer incurable. Moreover there is yet another accident. It happeneth that oftentimes the crust being fallen off, the flesh not being well renewed, the blood issueth out as much as it did before. But when they shall be tyed, the ligature

Of what the eschar is made.

falls not off untill first the flesh have very well covered them againe: which is prooved by *Galen*, saying, that

In the 5 book of his *Meth*.

escharoticke medicines which cause a crust or eschar, whensoever they fall off, leave the part more bare than the naturall habit requires. For the generation of a crust proceeds from the parts subject, and which are scituate round about it, being also burned, as I may say: wherefore by how much the part is burnt, by so much it looseth the

Words of the Adversary.

naturall heate. Then tell me when it is necessary to use escharoticke medicines, or cautering irons? Tis when the flux of blood is caused by erosion, or some Gangreene or putrifaction. Now is it thus? In fresh bleeding wounds there is neither Gangreene nor putrifaction. Therefore, the cauteries ought not to be there applyed. And when the Ancients commanded to apply hot irons to the mouthes of the vessells, it hath not beene onely to stay the flux of blood, but cheefely to correct the malignitie, or gangreenous putrifaction which might spoile the neighbouring parts. And it must be here noted, that if I had knowne such accidents to happen, which you have declared in your booke, in drawing and tying the vessells, I had never beene twice deceived; nor would I ever have left by my writings to posteritie, such a way of stopping a flux of blood: But I writ it after I had seene it done and did it very often, with happy successe. See then what may happen through your inconsiderate counsell, without examining, or standing upon the

Proposition of the Adversary.

facility of tying the sayd vessells. For see, heere's your scope and proposition, to tye the vessells after amputation is a new remedy, say you; then it must not be used, it is an ill argument for a Doctor.

But as for that (say you) one must use fire after the amputation of members, to consume, and drie the putrifaction, which is a common thing in Gangreenes, and mortifications, that indeed hath no place here, because the practise

In the 5. booke, ch. 26, and in the 7 booke, ch. 33.

is to amputate the part above that which is mortified, and corrupted; as *Celsus* writes and commands, to make the amputation upon the sound part, rather than to leave any whit of the corrupted. I would willingly aske you, if when a veine is cut transverse, and that it is very much retracted towards the originall, whether you would make no conscience to burne till that you had found the orifice of the veine, or artery; and if it be not more easie onely with a Crow bill to pinch and draw the vessell, and so tie it? In which you may openly shew your ignorance, and that you have your minde seised with much rancor and choler. We daily see the ligature of the vessells practised with happy successe after the amputation of a part, which I will now verifie by experiences and histories, of those to whom the said ligature hath beene made, and persons yet living.

In the ch. of cutting, booke the 2.

Experiences.

The 16. day of *June* 1582. in the presence of Master *John Liebaud* doctor in the faculty of Physicke at *Paris*, *Claud Viard* sworne Chirurgion, Master *Mathurin Huron*, Chirurgion of Monsieur *de Souvray*, and I, *John Charbonell* master Barber Chirurgion of *Paris*, well understanding the *Theoricke*, and *Practicke* of Chirurgery, did with good dexterity amputate the left legge of a woman tormented the space of three yeares with extreame paine, by reason of a great *Caries* which was in the bone *Astragal*, *Cuboides*, great and little *focile*,[1] and through all the nervous parts, through which she felt extreame and intollerable paines night and day: she is called *Mary* of *Hostel*, aged 28 yeares, or thereabouts, wife of *Peter Herve*, Esquire of the Kitchin to the Lady *Duchesse of Uzez*, dwelling in the streete of *Verbois* on the other side Saint *Martin* in the fields, dwelling at the signe of the Saint *Johns* head; where the sayd *Charbonell* cut off the sayd legge, the breadth of foure large fingers below the Knee, and after that he had incised the flesh, and sawed the bone, hee griped the Veine with the Crow bill, then the Artery, then tyed them; from whence I protest to God (which the company that were there, can witnesse) that in all the operation which was sodainely done, there

A notable history.

The operation of Charbonell.

---
[1] i.e. the tibia and fibula.

was not spilt one porrenger of blood; and I bid the sayd
Charbonell to let it bleed more, following the precept of
Hippocrates, that it is good in all wounds and also in inveterate ulcers, to let the blood runne; by this meanes, the
part is lesse subject to inflammation. The sayd *Charbonell*
continued the dressing of her, who was cured in two
moneths, without any fluxe of blood happening unto her,
or other ill accident; and she went to see you at your lodging being perfectly cured.

Another history of late memory, of a singing man of
our Ladyes Church named master *Paulain*,[1] who broke both
the bones of his legge which were crusht in divers peeces,
insomuch that there was no hope of cure: to withstand a
gangreene and mortification, and by consequence death.
Monsieur *Helin* Doctor, Regent in the faculty of Physicke,
a man of honour and of good knowledge, *Claud Viard*, and
Simon Peter, sworne Chirurgions of *Paris*, men well exercised in Chirurgery; and *Balthazar* of *Lestre*, and *Leonard
de Leschenal*, Master Barber Chirurgions, well experimented
in the operations of Chirurgery, were all of opinion to withstand the accidents aforesayd, to make entire amputation
of the whole legge, a little above the broken & shivered
bones & the torne nerves, veines, arteries; the operation
was nimbly done, by the sayd *Viard*, and the blood stancht
by the ligature of the vessells in the presence of the sayd
Helin, and master *Tonsard* great Vicar of our Ladyes
Church, and was continually drest by the sayd *Leschenal*,
and I went to see him other whiles; he was happily cured
without the application of hot irons, and walketh lustily on
a woodden legge.

*In the 7. sen-
tence of the
booke of
Ulcers.*

*Another
history.*

*Operation
done by
Viard.*

Another History.

In the yeare 1583. the 10. day of *December*, *Toussaint
Posson* borne at *Roinville*, at this present dwelling at *Beau-
vais* neare *Dourdan*, having his Legge all ulcered, and all the
bones cariez'd and rotten, prayed me for the honor of God

[1] Instead of this name the English text has *Colt.*

to cut off his Legge by reason of the great paine which he could no longer endure. After his body was prepared I caused his legge to be cut off, fowre fingers below the *rotula* of the knee, by *Daniel Poullet* one of my servants, to teach him and to imbolden him in such workes; and there he readily tyed the vessells to stay the bleeding, without application of hot irons, in the presence of *James Guillemeau* ordinary Chirurgion to the King, and *John Charbonell* master Barber Chirurgion of *Paris*: and during the cure was visited by Master *Laffilé* and Master *Courtin* Doctors, Regents in the facultie of Medicine at *Paris*. The said operation was made in the house of *John Gohell* Inkeeper, dwelling at the signe of the white horse in the Greve. I will not here forget to say, that the Lady Princesse of *Montpensier*, knowing that he was poore, and in my hands, gave him money to pay for his chamber and diet. He was well cured, God be praysed, and is returned home to his house with a woodden Leg.

Another History.

A Gangreene happened to halfe of the Legge to one named *Nicholas Mesnager* aged threescore and sixteene yeares, dwelling in *S. Honoré* street, at the signe of the Basket; which happened to him through an inward cause, so that wee were constrained to cut off his Legge to save his life: and it was taken off by *Anthony Renaud*, master Barber Chirurgion of *Paris* the 16. day of *December* 1583. in the presence of Master *Le Fort*, and Master *La Noüe* sworne Chirurgions of *Paris*; and the blood was stanched by the Ligature of the vessells, and hee is at this present cured and in health, walking with a woodden Leg.

Gangreene happening by an antecedent cause.

Another History.

A Waterman at the Port of *Nesle*, dwelling neare *Monsieur de Mas*, Postmaster, named *John Boussereau*, in whose hands a Musket brake asunder, which broke the bones of his hand, and rent and tore the other parts in such sort that

it was needfull and necessary to make amputation of the
hand two fingers above the wrist: which was done by

Operation
done by
Guillemeau.

James Guillemeau then Chirurgion in ordinary to the king,
who dwelt at that time with me. The operation likewise
being redily done, and the blood stancht by the Ligature of
the vessells without burning irons: hee is at this present
living.

Another History.

Operation
done by the
Author.

A Merchant Grocer dwelling in S^t. *Denis* street at the
signe of the great *Tournois* named the Judge, who fell upon
his head, where was made a wound neare the temporall
muscle, where he had an artery opened, from whence
issued forth blood with great impetuosity, in so much that
common remedies would not serve the turne; I was called
thither, where I found Master *Rasse*, Master *Cointeret*,
Master *Viard*, sworne Chirurgions of *Paris*, to stay the
blood; where presently I tooke a needle and thread, and
tyed the arterie, and it bled no more after that, and was
quickly cured. Master *Rousselet* can witnesse it, not long
since Deacon of your Facultie, who was in the cure with us.

Another History.

Another
operation.

A Sergeant of the Chastelet dwelling neare S. *Andrew des
Arts*, who had a stroake of a sword upon the throate in the
Clarkes' medow, which cut asunder the jugular veine
externe. As soone as he was hurt he put his handkercher
upon the wound, and came to looke for mee at my house,
and when hee tooke away his handkercher the blood leaped
out with great impetuosity: I suddainly tyed the veine
toward the roote; he by this meanes was stanched and cured
thankes be to God. And if one had followed your manner
of stanching blood by cauteries, I leave it to be supposed
whether he had been cured; I thinke hee had beene dead in
the hands of the operator. If I would recite all those whose
vessells were tyed to stay the blood which have beene cured,
I should not have ended this long time; so that me thinkes

there are Histories enough recited to make you beleeve the blood of veines and arteries is surely stanched without applying any actuall cauteries.

Du Bartas.

He that doth strive against experience,
Daignes not to talke of any learned science.

Now my little Master, seeing that you reproach me, that I have not written all the operations of Chirurgery in my workes which the Ancients writ of, I should be very sorry for it: for then indeede might you justly call me *Carnifex*. I have left them because they are too cruell, and am willing to follow the modernes, who have moderated such cruelty: which notwithstanding you have followed step by step, as appeareth by the operations here written, extracted from your booke, which you have drawne here and there from certaine ancient Authors, such as follow: and such as you have never practised nor seene.

The first operation.

To inveterate fluxions of the eyes, & Migrimes, *Paulus Ægineta* as also *Albucasis* command to make *Arteriotomie*, see here the words of the same *Ægineta*. You marke the Arteries which are behind the eares, then divide them in cutting to the very bone, and make a great incision the breadth of two fingers; which is the will also of *Aetius* that the incision be made transverse, cutting or incising the length of two fingers, even till that the Artery be found, as you command to bee done in your booke; but I holding the opinion of *Galen*, who commands to dresse the diseased quickly, safely and with the least paine that is possible, I teach the young Chirurgion the meanes to remedy such evills in opening the Arteries behind the eares, and those of the Temples, with one only incision, as a letting blood, and not to make a great incision and cut out worke for a long time.

Booke the 6. Chap. 4 and 5.

Booke 2. Chap. 4.

Booke 3, ch. 9, sect. 7.

In the 2. booke of the chap. of *Hypospatisme*. Booke 14, ch. last, of the Meth.

In the 4. chap. of the 15. booke of my worke.

The second operation.

Booke 6
chap. 7.
Booke 2,
chap. 5.
In the 2,
book chap of
Periscythisme.
To fluxions which are made a long time upon the eyes, *Paul Ægineta* and *Albucasis* command to make incision which they call *Periscythismos* or *Angiologie* of the Greekes; and see heere the words of *Paul*, In this operation first the head is shaved, then taking heede of touching the temporall muscles, a transverse incision must bee made, beginning at the left Temple and finishing at the right, which you have put in your booke word for word, without changing any thing: which sheweth openly you are a right woundmaker; as may be seene in the Chapter which you call the Crowne cut, which is made halfe round under the Coronall suture from one temple to the another even to the bone. In the 25. ch.
of the 8. book
of my
workes. Now I doe not teach such a cruell kind of remedy, but instruct the operator by reason, authority and notable proofe of a sure and certaine way to remedy such affections without butchering men in this kind.

The third.

Book 6.
chap. 44.
Booke 2,
chap. 3.
Booke 3.
chap. 22.
In the cure of the *Empyema*, *Paul Ægineta*, *Albucasis* and *Celsus* commanded to apply some 13. others 15. Cauteries to give issue to the matter contained in the breast, as the said *Celsus* in the aforesaid place appointeth for Asthmatick people, which is a thing out of all reason (with respect to their honour be it spoken) that since the Chirurgions scope is to give issue to the matter therein contained, there is no *Guido* of
Chauliac the 2.
treatise,
Doct. 1.
chap. 1. other question than to make apertion, to evacuate the matter in the most inferior part. I have shewed the young Chirurgion the meanes to doe it safely, without tormenting the patients for nothing.

The fourth.

Booke 6,
chap. 10.
Booke 6.
chap. 46,
Book 2,
chap. 47.
In Paps that are too great, *Paul Æginet* and *Albucasis* commands to make a crosse incision, to take out all the fat, and then joyne together the wound by stitch: In briefe, it is to flea a man alive, which I have never practised, nor counsell it to bee done by the young Chirurgion.

The fifth.

Albucasis and *Paul Æginet* will cauterize the Liver and the Spleene with hot irons, which the modernes have never practised; for indeede reason is manifestly repugnant thereunto.

In the first booke, chap. 29, & 30, also in booke 2, chap. 32. Booke 6, chap. 47, and 48.

The Sixth.

In the *Paracentesis* which is made in the third kind of Dropsie called *Ascites, Celius Aurelianus* commandeth divers apertions to be made in the belly. *Albucasis* applies nine actuall cauteries, that is to say, foure about the Navell, one upon the Stomacke, one upon the Spleene, one upon the Liver, two behind the backe upon the spondills, one of them neare the breast, the last neare the Stomacke. *Ætius* is likewise of the same opinion, to open the belly with divers cauteries. *Paul Æginet* commands to apply five actual cauteries to make the said *Paracentesis*. But abhorring such a kind of burning of which you speake much in your third booke, I shew another kind of practise, the which is done in making a simple incision in the sayd belly, as may be seene in my workes, with happy successe. I doe not teach yong men in my workes the manner of burning, which the Ancients have called *infibulare*, that is not in practise though *Celsus* writeth of it.

In the 5. book chap. 1, *De internis morbis*. Booke 1. chap. 33, Book 3, sect. 2, chap. 89.

Booke the 6, chap. 50.

Chap. 12. book 6.

In the 7. book chap. 25.

The Seaventh.

In the Sciaticke proceeding from an internall cause, and because the viscous humors displace the bones, *Paul* commands to burne or cauterize the said joynt to the bone: *Dioscorides* commands the same, Which I doe not finde expedient, taking indication from the subjacent parts: for there where one would burne, tis in the place of the foure twin muscles, under which passeth the great Nerve descending from the holy bone; which being burnt, I leave it to your censure what might happen, as *Galen* remarketh speaking of the *Ustion* which must be made in the shoulder called *humerus*.

Book 6, chap. 76. Book 2, chap. 72.

Upon the sentence 49, of the 1 section of the book of Arts.

The Eighth.

Sentence the
22, and 23,
of the 3
section of the
booke of the
joynts.

In the outward Laxation of the Spondills,[1] *Hippocrates*
commands to bind the man right upon a Ladder, the
Armes and Legges tyed and bound: then afterwards having
raised the Ladder to the top of a tower, or the ridge of an
house, with a great rope in a pully, then to let the patient
fall plumbe down upon the hard pavement; which *Hippocrates* sayes was done in his time. But I doe not shew any
such way of giving the strapado to men, but I shew the

Chap. 16, of
the 15, booke.

Chirurgion in my workes, the way to reduce them surely,
and without great paine. Moreover I should be sorry to
follow the saying of the sayd *Hippocrates*, in the third booke
De morbis, who commands in the disease called *Volvulus* to
cause the belly to bee blowne with a paire of Bellowes,
putting the nosell of them into the *intestinum rectum*, and
then blow there till the belly be much stretcht, afterwards
to give an emollient glister, and to stop the fundament
with a sponge. Such practise as this is not made now a
dayes, therefore wonder not if I have not spoken of it. And
you not being contented to patch together the operations
of the above said Authors, you have also taken divers in
my workes, as every man may know: which sheweth
manifestly that there is nothing of your owne in your
Chirurgions Guide. I leave out divers other unprofitable
operations which you quote in your booke, without knowing what beasts they are, in never having seene them
practised; but because you have found them written in the
bookes of the Ancients, you have put them into your booke.

Moreover you say that you will teach me my lesson in
the operations of Chirurgery, which I thinke you cannot
doe: because I have not onely learned them in my Study,
and by the hearing for many yeares the lessons of Doctors
of Physicke: but as I have sayd before in my Epistle to the
Reader, I was resident the space of three yeares in the
Hospitall of *Paris*, where I had the meanes to see and learne

[1] i.e. the vertebræ.

divers workes of Chirurgery, upon divers diseases, together
with the Anatomy, upon a great number of dead bodies,
as oftentimes I have sufficiently made triall publickly in the
Physitions schoole at *Paris*, and my good lucke hath made
mee seene much more. For being called to the service of
the Kings of France (foure of which I have served) I have
beene in company at Battells, Skirmishes, assaults, and be-
seiging of Citties and Fortresses; as also I have beene shut up
in Citties with those that have beene beseiged, having charge
to dresse those that were hurt. Also I have dwelt many
yeares in this great and famous Citty of *Paris*, where,
thankes bee to God, I have lived in very good reputation
amongst all men, and have not beene esteemed the least in
rancke of men of my profession, seeing there was not any
cure, were it never so difficult and great, where my hand
and my counsell have not beene required, as I make it
appeare in this my worke. Now dare you (these things
being understood) say you will teach mee to performe the
workes of Chirurgery, since you never went further than
your study? The operations of the same are foure in
generall (as we have declared heretofore) where you make
but three, that is to say, joyne that which is separated,
separate that which was conjoyned, and to take away that
which is superfluous, and the fourth which I make, is as
much necessary as industrious invention, to adde to Nature
that which is wanting, as I have shewed heere above. Also
it is your will that the Chirurgion make but the three
operations above sayd without medling to ordaine a simple
Cataplasme, saying it is that which comes to your part
belonging to the Physition: And that the Ancients (in the
discourse which you have made to the Reader) have
divided the practise of Physick into three kinds, that is to
say, Diet, Medicine, and Chirurgery. But I would willingly
demand of you, who hath made the partition, and where
any thing should be done, who are those which are content
with their part, without any enterprize upon the other?
For *Hippocrates*, *Galen*, *Ætius*, *Avicen*, in briefe, all the

Phisitions, as well Greekes and Latins as Arabians, have never so treated of the one, that they have not treated of the other, for the great affinitie and tye that there is betweene them two, and it should bee very difficult to doe otherwise. Now when you will vilifie Chirurgery so much, you speake against your selfe; for in your Epistle which you have dedicated to Monsieur of *Martigues*, you say, that Chirurgery is the most noble part of Physicke, as well by reason of the originall, antiquity, necessity, as certainty in her actions; for shee workes *Luce aperta*, as learnedly writeth *Celsus* in the beginning of his seaventh booke; therefore it is to be beleeved you never went out of your study, but to teach the *Theorick* (if you have beene able to doe it.)

A faire similitude.

The operations of Chirurgery are learn't by the eye, & by the touch. I will say that you much resemble a yong Lad of Low *Britany*, of plump buttocks, where was stuffe sufficient; who demanded leave of his father to come to *Paris*, to take *France*; being arrived the Organist of our Ladys Church, met with him at the Pallace gate, who took him to blow the Organs, where hee was remaining three yeeres: hee saw hee could somewhat speake *French*, he returnes to his father, and told him that he spake good *French*, and moreover he knew well, to play on the Organs: his father received him very joyfully, for that hee was so wise and learned in so short a time. Hee went to the Organist of their great Church, and prayed him to permit his sonne to play on the Organs, to the end he might know whether his sonne was become so skilfull a master, as he sayd he was; which the Organist agreed to very willingly. Being entred to the Organs, he cast himselfe with a full leape to the bellowes, the master Organist bid him play, and that he would blow; then this good master answeares, Let him play himselfe on the Organs if he would for him, hee could doe nothing but play on the bellowes. I thinke also my little master, that you know nothing else, but to prattle in a chaire; but I will play upon the keyes, and make the Organs sound (that is to say) I will doe the operations of Chirurgery, that which you cannot in any wise doe, because you have not gone from your study or the schooles, as I have sayd before. But also, as I have sayd already in the Epistle to the Reader, that the labourer doth little profit by talking of the seasons, discourse of the manner of tilling the earth, to shew what seedes are proper to each soyle; all which is nothing if he put not his hand to the Plough, and couple the Oxen together. So likewise is it no great matter if you doe not know the *Practicke*, for a man may execute Chirurgery well, although he have no tongue at all. As *Cornelius Celsus* hath very well remarked in his first booke when he saith, *Morbos non eloquentia, sed remedijs curari: quæ si quis elinguis, usu discretus bene norit, hunc aliquanto majorem medicum futurum, quàm si sine usu linguam suam excoluerit*; that is to say; Diseases are not to bee cured by eloquence, but by remedies well and duely applyed, which if any wise and discreete man though he have no tongue know well the use thereof, this man in time shall become the greater Physition, than if without practise his tongue were dipt with oratory; the which you your selfe confesse in your sayd booke by a Tetrasticke which is thus:[1]

> To talke's not all in Chirurgions Art,
> But working with the hands.
> Aptly to dresse each greeved part,
> And guide fire, knife, and bands.

Aristotle in the first booke of his Metaphysicks the first chapter saith, Experience is almost like unto science, and by the same, Art and science have beene invented. And indeed we see these which are experimented, attaine sooner to that which they intend, than those which have reason and not experience, because that the sayd experience is a knowledge of singular and particular things, and science on the contrary is a knowledge of things universall. Now that which is particular is more healeable than that which is

---

[1] Malgaigne points out that this quatrain is by Courtin, the translator of Gourmelen's book.

universall, therefore those which have experience are more wise and more esteemed, than those which want it, by reason they know what they doe. Moreover I say, that science without experience, bringeth no great assurance.

Alciat, a Doctor of *Milan*, boasted one day of himselfe, that his glory was greater and more famous than that of Counsellors, *Presidents*, masters of Request: because that it was by his science, and his instructions that they became such: but he was answeared by a Counsellor, that he was like unto a whetstone, which made the knife sharpe and ready to cut, not being able so to doe it selfe, and alledged the verses of *Horace* that:

> *Fungebatur vice cotis, acutum*
> *Reddere quæ ferrum valet, exors ipsa secandi.*

See you now (my little master) my answers to your calumniations, and pray you, if you beare a good minde (to the publicke good) to review and correct your booke, as soone as you can, and not to hold young Chirurgion in this errour by the reading of the same, where you teach them to use hot irons after the amputation of members, to stay a fluxe of blood, seeing there is another meanes, and not so cruell and more sure and easie. Moreover if to day after an assault of a Citty, where diverse Souldiers have had armes and legges broken, and shot off by Cannon Bullets, Cutlas or other instruments of warre; to stay the fluxe of blood, if you should use hot irons, it would be needful to have a forge, and much coales to heate them: and also the souldiers would hold you in such horror for this cruelty, that they would kill you like a Calfe, even as in times past they did to one of the chiefest Chirurgions of *Rome*,[1] which may be found written before in the third chapter of the Introduction of Chirurgery, the 1 booke. Now least the Sectators of your writings should fall into such inconveniencie, I pray them to follow the methode aforesayd, the which I have

---

[1] This refers to the story of Archagelus, who was stoned to death on the Field of Mars.

shewed to be true and certaine, and approved by authority, reason and experience.

The Voyage of Turin, 1537.

Moreover, I will heere shew to the readers the places where I have had meanes to learne the Art of Chirurgery, for the better instructing of the young Chirurgion: and first in the yeere 1536, the great King *Francis* sent a great Army to *Turin*, to recover the Cittyes and Castles, which the Marquesse of *Guast*, Lievtenant generall of the Emperor, had taken: where the high Constable of *France* the great master, was Lievtenant generall of the Army, and Monsieur *de Montejan* Colonel generall of the foote, of which I was then Chirurgion. A great part of the Army arrived in the Country of *Suze*; we found the enemy which stopt the passage, and had made certaine Forts, and trenches, insomuch that to hunt them out and make them leave the the place, we were forced to fight, where there were divers hurt and slaine, as well of the one side as of the other: but the enemies were constrayned to retire, and get into the Castle, which was caused partly by one Captaine *Ratt*, who climed with divers of the souldiers of his company upon a little Mountaine; there where he shot directly upon the enemies, hee received a shot upon the anckle of his right foote, wherewith presently he fell to the ground; and sayd then, Now is the *Rat* taken. I dressed him, and God healed him. We entred the throng in the Citty, and passed over the dead bodyes, and some which were not yet dead, we heard them cry under our horses feete, which made my heart relent to heare them. And truely I repented to have forsaken *Paris* to see so pittifull a spectacle. Being in the Citty, I entred into a stable thinking to lodge my owne, and my mans horse, where I found foure dead souldiers, and three which were leaning against the wall, their faces wholly disfigured, and neither saw nor heard, nor spoake; and their cloathes did yet flame with the gunpowder which had burnt them. Beholding them with pitty, there

The retiring of the enemies.

History.

happened to come an old souldier, who asked me if there were any possible meanes to cure them, I told him no: he presently approached to them, and gently cut their throates without choler. Seeing this great cruelty, I told him he was a wicked man, he answered me that he prayed to God, that whensoever he should be in such a case, that he might finde some one that would doe as much to him, to the end he might not miserably languish. And to returne to our former discourse, the enemie was sōmoned to render, which they soon did, & went out, their lives onely saved, with a white staffe in their hands; the greatest part whereof went and got to the Castle of *Villane*, where there was about 200. Spaniards; Monsieur the Constable would not leave them behind, to the end that the way might be made free. This Castle is seated upon a little mountaine, which gave great assurance to them within, that one could not plant the Ordinance to beate upon it, and were sommoned to render, or that they should be cut in peeces; which they flatly refused, making answere that they were as good and faithfull servants to the Emperor, as Monsieur the Constable could bee to the King his master. Their answere heard, they made by force of arme, two great Cannons to be mounted in the night with cords and ropes, by the Swissers and Lansquenets; when as the ill lucke would have it, the two Cannons being seated, a Gunner by great negligence set on fire a great bagge of Gunpowder; wherewith he was burned together with ten or twelve souldiers; and moreover the flame of the powder was a cause of discovering the Artillery, which made them that all night, they of the Castle did nothing but shoote at that place where they discovered the two peeces of Ordinance, wherewith they kild and hurt a great number of our people.

The next day early in the morning a Battery was made, which in a few houres made a breach, which being made they demanded to parly with us; but twas too late for them; For in the meane time our French foote, seeing them amazed, mounted to the breach, and cut them all in peeces,

Brave answere of the Souldiers.

except a faire young lusty mayd of *Piedmount*, which a Exemplary punishment. great Lord would have kept and preserved for him to keepe him company in the night, for feare of the greedy wolfe. The Captaine and Ensigne were taken alive, but soone after were hanged upon the gate of the Citty, to the end they might give example and feare to the Imperiall souldiers not to bee so rash and foolish, to be willing to hold such places against so great a Army. Now all the sayd souldiers of the Castle, seeing our people comming with a most violent fury, did all their endeavour to defend themselves, they kild and hurt a great company of our souldiers, with Pikes, Muskets, and stones, where the Chirurgions had good store of worke cut out. Now at that time I was a fresh water Souldier, I had not yet seene wounds made by gun-shot at the first dressing. It is true, I had read in *John de Vigo*, in the first booke of wounds in generall, the eighth Counsell of De Vigo. chapter, that wounds made by weapons of fire did participate of Venenosity, by reason of the pouder, and for their cure commands to cauterize them with oyle of Elders scalding hot, in which should be mingled a little Treackle; and not to faile, before I would apply of the sayd oyle, knowing that such a thing might bring to the Patient great paine, I was willing to know first, before I applyed it, how the other Chirurgions did for the first dressing, which was to apply the sayd oyle the hottest that was possible into the wounds, with tents and setons; insomuch that I tooke courage to doe as they did. At last I wanted oyle, and was constrained in steed thereof, to apply a disgestive of yolkes of egges, oyle of Roses, and Turpentine. In the night I could not sleepe in quiet, fearing some default in not cauterizing, that I should finde those to whom I had not used the burning oyle dead impoysoned; which made me Experience of a bold man's happy successe. rise very early to visit them, where beyond my expectation I found those to whom I had applyed my digestive medicine, to feele little paine, and their wounds without inflammation or tumor, having rested reasonable well in the night: the others to whom was used the sayd burning oyle,

I found them feverish, with great paine and tumour about the edges of their wounds. And then I resolved with my selfe never so cruelly, to burne poore men wounded with gunshot. Being at *Turin* I found a Chirurgion, who had the fame above all others, for the curing of wounds of Gunshot, into whose favour I found meanes to insinuate my selfe, to have the receipt of his balme, as he called it wherewith he dressed wounds of that kind, and hee held me off the space of two yeeres, before I could possible draw the receipt from him. In the end by gifts and presents he gave it me, which was this, to boyle young whelpes new pupped, in oyle of Lillies, [with] earth wormes prepared with

Receipt of an excellent balme for wounds with Gunshot.

Turpentine of *Venice.* Then was I joyfull and my heart made glad, that I had understood his remedy, which was like to that which I had obtained by great chance. See then how I have learned to dresse wounds made with gunshot, not by bookes. My Lord Marshall of *Montejan* remained Lieutenant generall for the King in *Piedmont*, having ten or twelve thousand men in garrison through the Cittyes and Castles, who often combated with swords and other weapons, as also with muskets; and if there were foure hurt, I had alwayes three of them, and if there were question of cutting off an arme or a legge, or to trepan, or to reduce a fracture or dislocation, I brought it well to passe. The sayd Lord Marshall sent me one while this way, another while that way, for to dresse the appointed Souldiers which were beaten as well in other Cittes as that of *Turin*, insomuch that I was alwayes in the Countrey one way or other. Monsieur the Marshall sent for a Physition to *Milan*, who had no lesse reputation in the medicinall Art (than the deceased Monsieur *le Grand*) to take him in hand for an hepaticall flux, whereof at last he dyed. This Physitian was a certaine while at *Turin* to deale with him, and was often called to visite the hurt people, where he alwayes found me, and I consulted with him, and some other Chirurgions, and when wee had resolved to doe any serious worke of Chirurgery, twas *Ambroise Paré* that put his hand thereto, where I did it promptly and with dexterity, and with a great assurance, in so much that the sayd Physition admired me, to see me so ready in the operation of Chirurgery, seeing the small age which I had. One day discoursing with the sayd Lord Marshall, he sayd to him, *Signor, tu hai un Chirurgico giovane di anni, ma egli è vecchio di sapere è di esperientia. Guardalo bene, perche egli ti fara servicio & honore.* That is to say, Thou hast a young Chirurgion of age, but he is old in knowledg and experience, preserve him well; for he will doe thee service, and honour. But the old man knew not that I had dwelt three yeares in the Hospitall of *Paris*, there to dresse the diseased. In the end Monsieur *Marshall* dyed with his hepaticall fluxe. Being dead, the King sent Monsieur the Marshall of *Annebaut* to be in his place, who did me this honour to pray me to dwell with him, and that he would use me as well or better, than Monsieur the Marshall *Montejan*; which I would not doe for the greefe I had for the losse of my master who loved me intimately, and I him in the like manner; and so I came backe to *Paris*.

Witnesse of the dexterity of the Author.

The death of Marshall Montejan.

The Voyage of Marolle *and of low* Brittany, 1543.

I went to the Camp of *Marolle*, with the deceased Monsieur *de Rohan*, where King *Francis* was in person, and I was Chirurgion of the company of the sayd Monsieur *de Rohan*. Now the King was advertized by Monsieur *de Estampes*, governour of *Brittany*, that the *English* had hoyste Sayle to land in Low *Brittany*, and prayed him that he would send Monsieur *de Rohan*, and Monsieur *de Laval* for succour, because they were the Lords of that Countrey, and for their sakes those of that Country would beate backe the enemy and keepe them from landing. Having received this advertisement, his Majesty dispatched to send the sayd Lords for the releefe of their Countrey, and to each was given as much power as to the Governour; in so much that they were all three the Kings Lieutenants. They tooke willingly this charge upon them, and speedily went away in Poste, and

lead me with them to *Landreneau*, there where we found
every one in armes, the Alarum bells sounding on every
side, yea five or sixe leagues about the *Harbors*, that is to
say, *Brest, Couquet, Crozon, Le Fou, Doulac, Laudanec,* each
of them well furnisht with Artillery, as Cannons, Demy-
cannons, Culverins, Sakers, Serpentines, Falcons, Harque-
buzes, in breefe there was nothing wanting in Artillery, or
souldiers aswell *Brittanes* as *French,* to hinder that the
English made no landing, as they had resolved at their
parting from *England.* The enemies Army came unto the
very mouth of the Cannon, and when we perceived them
that they would land, they were saluted with Cannonshot,
and we disovered our men of warre, together with our

The English
retire.

Artillery: they fled to Sea againe, where I was glad to see
their vessells hoise saile againe, which was in a great number and in good order, and seemed like a Forest which
marched upon the Sea. I saw a thing also whereat I mar-
veiled much, which was that the bullets of great peeces
made great rebounds, and grazed upon the water as upon
the ground. Now to make the matter short, the English
did us no harme, and returned whole and sound into
England, and left us in peace.We stayd in that Countrey in
garrison, till we were assured that their army was dispersed.
In the meane time our horsemen exercised their feates of
activity, as to run at the ring, fight in duell, and others, so
that there was still something to imploy me withall. Monsieur *de Estampes,* to make sport and pleasure to the sayd
Monsieur *de Rohan,* and *Laval,* and other gentlemen,
caused diverse Countrey wenches, to come to the feasts,

Dances of th
Countrey
Wenches.

to sing songs in the Low *Brittan* tongue, where their har-
mony was like the croaking of Frogges, while they are in
love. Moreover he made them dance the *Brittany Triary,*
without mooving feete or buttockes, hee made them heare

Wrastlers;
little *Brittan*
a good
wrastler.

and see much good. Otherwhiles they caused the Wrastlers
of the Cittyes, and Townes, to come where there was a
Prize for the best, and the sport was seldome ended, but
that one or other had a legge or an arme broken, or the

shoulder or hippe displaced; there was a little man of Low *Brittany* of a square body and well set, who held a long time the credit of the field, and by his skill, and strength, threw five or sixe to the ground; there came to him a great schoolemaster, who was sayd to be one of the best wrastlers of all *Brittany*: he entred into the lists, having taken off his long jacket, in hose and doublet, and being neere the little man, he seemed as if he had beene tyed to his girdle. Notwithstanding when each of them tooke hold of the collar, they were a long time without doing anything, and they thought they would remaine equall in force and skill: but the little man cast himselfe with an ambling leape under this great Pedant, and tooke him on his shoulder, and cast him on his Kidneyes spread abroad like a frogge, and then all the company laught at the skill and strength of this little fellow. This great *Dativo* had a great spight, for being cast by so little a man: he rose againe in choler, and would have his revenge. They tooke hold againe of each others collar, and were againe a good while at their hold without falling to ground: in the end this great man let himselfe fall upon the little, and in falling put his elbow upon the pitch of his stomacke, and burst his heart, and kild him starke dead. The little *Brittan* kild. And knowing he had given him his deathes blow, tooke againe his long cassocke, and went away with his tayle betweene his legges and hid himselfe, seeing that the little man came not againe to himselfe, either for Wine, Vinegar or any other thing that was presented unto him; I drew neere to him, and felt his pulse which did not beate at all, then I sayd he was dead; then the *Brittanes* who assisted the wrastling sayd aloud in their jabbering, that is not in the sport. And some sayd that the sayd Pedagoge was accustomed to doe so, and that but a yeere passed he had done the like in a wrastling. I would needes open the body to know the cause of this sodaine death, where I found much blood in the *Thorax* and in the inferiour belly, and I strived to finde out any apertion in the place, from whence might issue so great a quantity of blood, which I could not

The body opened by the Author.

doe for all the dilligence I could make. Now I beleeve it
was *per Diapedesin* or *Anastomosin*, that is to say by, the
apertion of the mouthes of the vessells, or by their porosi-
ties;[1] the poore little wrastler was buryed. I tooke leave of
Messieurs de Rohan, de Laval, and *Estamps*. Monsieur *de
Rohan*, gave mee a present of fifty double duckets, and an
ambling horse, and Monsieur *de Laval* another for my
man, and Monsieur *de Estamps*, a Diamond of thirty
Crownes, and so I returned to my house at *Paris*.

The Voyage of Perpignan, 1542.[2]

A little while after Monsieur *de Rohan* tooke me with
him poste, to the campe of *Perpignan*; being there, the
enemy made a Sally forth, and came and inclosed three
peeces of our Artillery, where they were beaten back, to
the gates of the Citty: which was not done without hurting
and killing many, and amongst the rest *de Brissac*, (who was
then chiefe master of the Artillery) received a musket shot
upon the shoulder: returning to his Tent, all the others that
were hurt followed him, hoping to be drest by the Chirurgions, that ought to dresse them. Being come to his Tent
and layd on his bed, the bullet was searched for by three or
foure the most expert Chirurgions of the Army, who could
not finde it, but sayd it was entred into his body.

Addresse of
the Author.

In the end hee called for me, to see if I were more skilfull
than them, because he had knowne me before in *Piedmount*: by and by I made him rise from his bed, and prayed
him to put his body into that posture as it was then when
hee received his hurt; which he did taking a javelin betweene
his hands as he held the Pike in the skirmish. I put my hand
about the wound, and found the bullet in the flesh, making
a little tumor under the *Omoplate*:[3] having found it I shewed
them the place where it was, and it was taken out by
Master *Nicholas Lavernault* Chirurgion to Monsieur the

[1] Paré has here reversed the meanings of Galen's terms.
[2] Misdated by Peré 1543. It took place before the Journey to Marolle.
[3] i.e. the Scapula.

Dolphin, who was the Kings Lieutenant in that army, yet notwithstanding the honour remained to me for finding of it.

I saw one thing of great remark, which is this: that a souldier in my presence gave to one of his fellowes a stroake with an Halbard upon the head, penetrating even to the left ventricle of the braine, without falling to the ground. Hee that strooke him said he had heard that he had cheated at Dice, and that he had drawne a great summe of money, and that it was his custome to cheate; I was called to dresse him, which I did as it were for the last, knowing well that he would quickly die: having drest him he returned all alone to his lodging, which was at least two hundred paces distant: I bid one of his companions send for a Priest to dispose of the affaires of his soule; he helpt him to one who stayd with him to the last gaspe. The next day the patient sent for mee by his shee friend in a boyes apparell to come to dresse him, which I would not doe, fearing hee should die under my hands; and to put it off, I sayd I must not take off the dressing till the third day, by reason hee would die though hee were never touched. The third day hee came staggering, and found me in my Tent accompanied with his wench, and prayed mee most affectionately to dresse him: And shewed me a purse wherein he had an hundred or sixscore peeces of Gold, and that he would content me to my desire; for all that, yet notwithstanding I left not off to deferre the taking off his dressing, fearing least hee should die at the same instant. Certaine Gentlemen desired me to goe dresse him, which I did at their request, but in dressing him he died under my hands in a Convulsion. Now this Priest accompanied him untill death, who seazed upon the purse for feare least another should take it, saying, hee would say Masses for his soule. Moreover hee furnisht himselfe with his cloathes, and with all the rest of his things. I have recited this History as a monstrous thing, that the Souldier fell not to ground when he had received this great stroake, and was in good senses

History.

even till death. Soone after, the Campe was broken for
divers causes; the one because we were advertized that
foure companies of *Spaniards* were entred into *Perpignan*;
the other, that the Plague begun much in our Campe, and
it was told us by the people of the countrey that shortly
there would bee a great overflowing of the Sea, which
might drowne us all; and the presage which they had, was a
very great winde from Sea, which arose in such manner
that there remained not one Tent which was not broken
and overthrowne, for all the strength and dilligence that
could be given; and the Kitchins being all uncovered, the
winde raised so the dust and sand which salted and poudred
our meate, in such sort that wee could not eate it, so that
wee were constrained to boile it in pots and other vessells
well covered.

Now we did not uncampe our selves in so good time,
but that there were many Carts and Carters Mules, and Mule
drivers drowned in the Sea, with great losse of baggage.
The Campe broken, I returned to *Paris*.

The Voyage to Landresy. 1544.

King *Francis* raised a great Army to victuall *Landresy*: on
the other side the Emperour had no lesse people, yea much
more; that is to say, eighteene thousand *Germans*, tenne
thousand *Spaniards*, sixe thousand *Wallons*, tenne thousand
English, and a matter of thirteene or foureteene thousand
Horse. I saw the two Armies neare one another, within
Canon shot, and it was thought they would never part
without giving battaile. There were some certaine foolish
Gentlemen who would approach the enemies Campe; certaine shot was made at them, and some dyed at the place,
others had their Legges or Armes carried away. The King
having done what hee desired, which was to revictuall
Landresy, retired himselfe with his Army to *Guise*, which
was the day after All Saints, one thousand five hundred
forty foure, and from thence I returned to *Paris*.

The Voyage of Boulogne. 1545.

A little while after we went to *Boulogne*, where the *English* seeing our Army, left the Forts which they had, that is to say, *Moulambert*; the little Paradise, *Monplaisir*, the fort of *Chatillon*, the *Portet*, the Fort *Dardelot*. One day going through the Campe to dresse my hurt people, the enemies who were in the Tower of *Order*, shot off a peece of Ordinance, thinking to kill two horsemen which stayd to talke one with another. It happened that the Bullet passed very neare one of them, which threw him to the ground, and t'was thought the said Bullet had toucht him, which it did not at all, but onely the winde of the said Bullet in the midst of his coate, which went with such a force that all the outward part of the Thigh became blacke and blew, and had much adoe to stand. I drest him, and made him divers Scarifications to evacuate the contused blood, which the winde of the said Bullet had made; and the rebounds that it made on the ground, kild foure souldiers which remained dead in the place. I was not farre from this stroake, so that I felt somewhat the mooved aire, without doing mee any harme, than a little feare which made me stoope my head very low, but the Bullet was already passed farre beyond mee.

The Souldiers mock't me to be affraid of a Bullet already gone. (My little Master) I thinke if you had beene there, that I had not been affraid alone, and that you would have had your share of it. What shall I say more? Monsieur the Duke of *Guise*, *Francis* of *Lorraine*, was hurt before *Bullogne* with a stroake of a Lance, which above the right eye, declining towards the nose, entred and pass'd quite through on the other side betweene the *nucha* and the eare, with so great a violence, that the head of the Lance with a great part of the wood was broken and remained within, in such sort that it could not bee drawne out but with great force, yea with Smithes pincers. Notwithstanding all this violence which was not done without breaking of bones, nerves, and arteries, and other parts; my said Lord, by the

The hurt of Monsieur *de Guise*.

helpe of God was cured: the said Lord went alwayes with open face, which was the cause that the Lance went through on the other side.

The voyage of Germany. 1552.

I went the voyage to *Germany* in the yeare 1552. with Monsieur *De Rohan* Captaine of 50. horse, where I was Chirurgion of his company, which I have said already. In this voyage Monsieur the high Constable of *France* was Generall of the Army: Monsieur *de Chastillon*, since Admirall, was chiefe Colonell of the foote, having foure Regiments of Lansquenets, under the conduct of these Captaines, *Recrod* and *Ringrave*, having each of them two Regiments, each Regiment was of tenne Ensignes, and each Ensigne of five hundred men. And besides these, was Captaine *Chartel*, who conducted the troopes that the Protestant Princes had sent to the King. This was a very faire company on foote, accompanied with fifteene hundred Horse, with the following of each one two Archers, which might make foure thousand five hundred Horse, besides two thousand Light horse, and as many Muskettieres on horsebacke, of whom Monsieur *de Aumalle* was Generall, besides the great number of Nobility who came for their pleasure. Moreover, the King was accompanied with two hundred Gentlemen of his house, & likewise with divers Princes; there was also for his troope that served him, the *French*, *Scottish*, and *Swissers* Guards, amounting to sixe hundred men on foote, and the companies of Monsieur the *Dolphin*, *Messieurs de Guise*, *de Aumalle*, and of the Marshall S. *André*, which amounted to foure hundred Lances, which was a mervelous thing to see such a faire Company; and in this equipage the King entred into *Thoul* and *Mets*. I will not omit to tell that it was ordained, that the Companions of *Messieurs de Rohan*, of the Count of *Sancerre*, of *Jarnac*, which was each of them of fifty horse, went by the Wings of the Campe; and God knowes we had scarcitie of victualls, and I protest to God that at three divers times I had thought I should have beene famisht, and it was not for want of money for I had enough, and we could not have victualls but by force, by reason that the *Pesants* withdrew it all into the Citties and Castles.

One of the servants of a Captaine of the company of Monsieur *de Rohan*, went with others thinking to enter into a Church where the *Pesants* were retired, thinking to finde victualls by force or love: but amongst the rest this man was well beaten, and returned with seaven wounds, with a sword in the head; the least of which penetrated the second table of the scull, and he had foure other upon the armes, and upon the right shoulder, which cut more than one halfe of the blade-bone, or *Omoplate*. He was brought backe to his masters lodging, who seeing of him so wounded, and that they were to depart thence the morrow after at the breake of day, and not thinking ever he could be cured, made him a grave, and would have cast him therein, saying that, or else the *Pesants* would massacre and kill him; I mov'd with pitty told him that he might yet be cured if he were well drest: divers Gentlemen of the company prayd him that he would cause him to bee brought along with the Baggage, seeing I had the willingnesse to dresse him; to which he agreed, and after that I had cloth'd him, he was but put into a Cart upon a bed well covered and well accommodated, which one horse did draw. I did the office of a Physition, Apothecary, Chirurgion, and Cooke; I drest him even to the end of his cure, and God cured him, in so much that all these three Companies admired at this cure. The horsemen of the company of Monsieur *de Rohan*, the first muster that was made, gave me each one, one Crowne, and the Archers halfe a Crowne.

The voyage of Danvilliers. 1552.

At the returne from the *German* Campe, King *Henry* beseiged *Danvilliers*, those within would not render. They were well beaten and our pouder failed us, in the meane time they shot much at our people. There was a Culverin shot pass'd a traverse the Tent of Monsieur *de Rohan*, which hit a Gentlemans Leg, which was of his traine; which I was faine to finish the cutting off, the which was done without applying hot irons.

Another
History.
The King sent for pouder to *Sedan*, which being come they began a greater battery than before, in such sort that they made a breach. *Messieur de Guise*, and the high Constable being in the Kings Chamber, told him they concluded the next day to make assault, & that they were assured they should enter into it, & that they should keep it secret lest the enemy were advertized. And all of them promised not to speake of it to any one. Now there was a Groome of the Kings chamber who lay under the Kings bed in the Camp to sleep, understood that they resolved the next day to give an assault, he presently revealed it to a certaine Captaine and told him that for certaine the day following assault should be given, & that he had heard it of the King, & praid the said Captaine that he would not speake a word of it to any body, which he promised; but his promise was not kept, for at the same instant, he went and declared it to a Captaine, & this Captaine to another Captaine, and from the Captaines to some of the Souldiers, saying alwayes, say nothing. It was so well hid that the next day early in the morning there was seene the greatest part of the Souldiers with their round hose and their breeches cut at knee for the better mounting at the breach. The King was advertiz'd of the rumor which runne through the Campe, that the assault must be given, whereof hee much mervailed, seeing there was but three of that advise, which had promised one to another, not to tell it to any one. The King sent for Monsieur *de Guise*, to know if hee had not talked of this assault; hee swore and affirmed to him he had not told it to any body; and Monsieur the Constable said as much; who said to the King he must expressely know who had declared this secret counsell; seeing they were but three. Inquisition was made from Captaine to Captaine, in the end the truth was found; for

one sayd twas such a one told me, another sayd as much, till at length they came to the first, who declared he had learnd it of a Groome of the Kings chamber, named *Guyard*, borne at *Blois*, the sonne of the deceased King *Francis* his Barber. The King sent for him into his Tent, in the presence of Monsieur *de Guise*, and of Monsieur the Constable, to understand from him whence he had it, and who told him that this assault was to bee given. The King told him that if he did not tell the truth, that he would cause him to be hanged; then he declared, he lay downe under his bed thinking to sleepe, and so having heard it, he declared it to a Captaine who was a friend of his, to the end hee might prepare himselfe with his Souldiers the first for the assault. After the King knew the truth; he told him, he should never serve him againe, and that he deserved to be hanged, and forbid him ever to come againe to the Court. My Groome of the Chamber went away with this sad newes, and lay with one of the Kings Chirurgions in ordinary, named Master *Lewis*, and in the night gave him-selfe six wounds with a knife, and cut his throate; yet the said Chirurgion perceived nothing till morning, till hee saw the bed bloody, and the dead body by him: hee much mervailed at this spectacle upon his waking, and was afraid least they should say he was the cause of this murther; but was soone freed, knowing the cause to bee from despera-tion, having lost the good amitie which the King bore to him. The said *Guyard* was buried. And those of *Danvilliers* when they saw the breach large enough for them to enter in, and the Souldiers prepared for the assault, yeelded them-selves to the mercy of the King. The chiefe of them were prisoners, and the Souldiers sent away without armes. The Campe being broken up I returned to *Paris* with my Gentleman whose Leg I had cut off, I drest him and God cured him; I sent him to his house merry with a woodden Leg, and was content, saying that he scaped good cheape, not to have beene miserably burnt, as you write in your booke, my little Master.

What it is to reveale the secrets of Princes.

The Voyage of Castle the Compt,[1] 1552.

A little while after King *Henry* levied an Army of thirty
thousand men, to goe make spoile about *Hedin.* The King
of *Navarre* who was then called Monsieur *de Vendosme,* was
chiefe of the Army, and the Kings Lieutenant. Being at
S. *Denis* in *France,* staying while the companies pass'd by,
he sent for me to *Paris* to come speak with him; being
there, he prayed me, and his request was a command, that
I would follow him this voyage; and I about to make my
excuse told him my wife was sicke in her bed, he made
me answer, that there were Physitions at *Paris* for to cure
her; and that he as well left his owne, who was as well
descended as mine; promising me that hee would use me
well, and forthwith gave command that I should be lodged
as one of his Traine. Seeing this great affection, which he
had to leade me with him, I durst not to refuse him. I went
and met with him at the Castle of *Compt,* within 3. or 4.
leagues of *Hedin,* there where there was the Emperors
Souldiers in garrison with a number of *Pesants* round
about: hee caused them to be summond to render themselves; and they made answer they should never have them
but by peeces, and let them doe their worst, and they would
doe their best to defend themselves. They put confidence
in their ditches full of water, and in two houres with a great
number of Bavins,[2] and certaine empty Caskes, way was
made to passe over the foote: when they must goe to the
assault and were beaten with five peeces of Cannon, till a
breach was made large enough to enter in, where they
within received the assault very valiantly, and not without
killing and hurting a great number of our people with
musket shot, pikes and stones. In the end when they saw
themselves constrained, they put fire to their pouder and

munition, which was the cause of burning many of our
people, and of theirs likewise, and they were all almost put
to the edge of the sword. Notwithstanding some of our

---

[1] The Château le Compte near Hesdin.   [2] i.e. faggots.

Souldiers had taken twentie or thirtie, hoping to have
ransome for them. That was knowne, and ordered by the
Counsell that it should be proclaimed by the Trumpet
throught the Campe, that all Souldiers who had any
Spaniards prisoners were to kill them, upon paine to be
hanged and strangled, which was done upon cold blood.
From thence we went and burnt divers Villages, whose
barnes were full of all kind of graine, to my great greefe.
Wee went along even to *Tournahan*, where there was a very
great Tower where the Enemies retired, but there was no
man found in it, all was pillaged, and the Tower was made
to leape by a Mine, and then with Gunpouder turned topsy
turvy. After that, the Campe was broken up, and I returned
to *Paris*. I will not yet forget to write that the day after the
Castle of *Compt* was taken, Monsieur *de Vendosme* sent a
Gentleman to the King to make report to him of all which
had pass'd, and amongst other things, told the King that I
had greatly done my duty in dressing those that were
wounded, and that I had shewed him eighteene Bullets
which I had taken or drawne out of the hurt bodies, and
that there were divers more which I could neither finde,
nor draw out, and told more good of mee than there was
by halfe. Then the King said hee would have mee into his
service, and commanded Monsieur *de Goguier* his chiefe
Physition to write me downe as entertained one of his
Chirurgions in ordinary, and that I should goe meete with
him at *Rheimes* within ten or twelve dayes; which I did,
where he did me the honour to command me that I would
dwell neare him, and that he would doe me good. Then I
thankt him most humbly for the honour it pleased him to
doe me, in calling me to his service.

The Voyage of Metz, 1552.

The Emperour having beseiged *Metz*, and in the hardest
time of winter, as each one knowes of fresh memory: and
that there was in the Citty five or sixe thousand men, and
amongst the rest seaven Princes; that is to say, Monsieur the

The taking of Castle of *Compt*.

The names of the Princes who were at the seige of *Metz*.

Duke of *Guise* the Kings Lieutenant, *Messieurs d' Anguien, de Condé, de Montpensier, de La Roch-upon-Yon*, Monsieur *de Nemours*, and divers other Gentlemen, with a number of old Captaines of warre, who often made sallies forth upon the enemies, (as wee shall speake of hereafter) which was not done without slaying many, as well on the one side as the other. For the most part all our wounded people dyed, and it was thought the medicaments wherewith they were dressed were poysoned; which caused Monsieur *de Guise* and other Princes to send to the King for mee, and that hee would send me with Drogues to them, for they beleeved theirs were poysoned, seeing that of their hurt people few escaped. I doe not beleeve there was any poyson, but the great stroakes of the Cutlasses, Musket shot, and the extremity of cold were the cause. The King caused one to write to Monsieur the Marshall of S. *André* which was his Lieutenant at *Verdun*, that hee found some meanes to make me enter into *Metz*. The said Lord Marshall of S. *André*

Nota.

and Monsieur the Marshall of old *Ville*, got an *Italian* Captaine, who promised them to make me enter in, which he did, and for which hee had fifteene hundred Crownes: the King having heard of the promise which the *Italian* Captaine had made, sent for mee and commanded me to take of his Apothecary named *Daigue* such, and as many Drogues as I should thinke fit for the hurt who were beseiged, which I did, as much as a posthorse could carry. The King gave me charge to speake to Monsieur *de Guise* and to the Princes, and Captaines who were at *Metz*. Being arrived at *Verdun*,

Commission of the Author.

a few dayes after Monsieur the Marshall of S. *André*, caused horses to be given to mee, and my man and for the *Italian*, who spake very good high *Dutch*, *Spanish* and *Walon* with his owne naturall tongue. When we were within eight or tenne Leagues of *Metz*, wee went not but in the night, and being neare the Campe, I saw a league and a halfe off bright fires round about the Citty, which seemed as if all the earth were on fire, and I thought wee could never passe through those fires without being discovered, and by consequent be hanged and strangled, or cut in peeces, or pay a great ransome. To speake truth, I wished my selfe at *Paris*, for the eminent danger which I foresaw. God guided so well our affaires that wee entred into the Citty at midnight with a certaine Token, which the Captaine had with another Captaine of the company of Monsieur *de Guise*: which Lord I went to, and found him in bed, who received me with great thankes, being joyfull of my comming. I did my message to him of all that the King had commanded me to say to him; I told him I had a little letter to give him, and that the next day I would not faile to deliver it him. That done he commanded mee a good lodging, and that I should be well used, and bid mee I should not faile to be the next day upon the Breach, where I should meete with all the Princes, and divers Captaines, which I did; who received me with great joy, who did mee the honour to imbrace me, and tell me I was very welcome, adding withall they did not feare to dye if they should chance to be hurt. Monsieur *de La Roch-upon-Yon* was the first that feasted me, and inquired of me what they sayd at the Court concerning the Citty of *Metz*; I told him what I thought good. Then presently he desired mee to goe see one of his Gentlemen, named Monsieur *de Magnane* at this present Knight of the Kings order, and Lieutenant of his Majesties Guard; who had his Leg broken by a Cannon shot. I found him in his bed, his Leg bended and crooked, without any dressing upon it; because a Gentleman promised him cure, having his name, and his girdle, with certaine words. The poore Gentleman wept, and cryed History. with paine which he felt, nor sleeping either night or day, in foure dayes: then I mock't at this imposture and false promise. Presently I did so nimbly restore and dresse his Legge, that he was without paine and slept all night, and since (thanks be to God) was cured, and is yet at this present living, doing service to the King. The said Lord of the *Roch-upon-Yon* sent me a Tunne of wine to my lodging, and bid tell me, when it was dronken hee would send mee another. That done, Monsieur *de Guise* gave me a list of certaine Captaines and Lords, and commanded me to tell them what the King had given me in charge; which I did, which was to doe his commendations and a thanksgiving for the duty they had done, and did in the keeping of the Citty of *Metz*, and that he would acknowledge it. I was more than eight daies in acquitting my charge, because they were many; first to the Princes and others, as the Duke *Horace*, the Count of *Martigues*, and his brother, Monsieur *de Baugé*, the Lords *Montmorancy*, and *d'Anville*, then Marshall of *France*, Monsieur *de La Chapel aux Ursins, Bonnivet, Carouge* now Governour of *Rohan*, the *Vidasme* of *Chartres*, the Count of *Lude*, Monsieur *de Biron* now Marshall of *France*, Monsieur *de Randan*, the *Rochfoucaut, Bordaille, d'Etrez*, the yonger, Monsieur *de S. John* in *Dolphiny*, & many others which it would bee too long to recite; and chiefely to divers Captaines who had very well done their duty in defence of their lives, and Citty. I demanded afterwards of Monsieur *de Guise*, what it pleased I should doe with the Drogues which I had brought, he bid me impart them to the Chirurgions and Apothecaries, and chiefely to the poore hurt Souldiers in the Hospitall which were in great number; which I did, and can assure you, I could not doe so much as goe see them, but they sent for mee to visit and dresse them. All the beseiged Lords prayed mee carefully to sollicite above all others Monsieur *de Pienne* who was hurt at the breach by a stone raised by a Cannon shot in the Temple with a fracture, and depression of the bone. They told mee that presently when hee received the stroake, hee fell to the earth as dead, and cast blood out of his mouth, nose, and eares with great vomitings, and was foureteene dayes without speaking one word, or having any reason; there happened to him also startings somewhat like Convulsions, and had all his face swell'd and livid. Hee was trepan'd on the side of the temporall muscle upon the *Os Coronale*. I drest him with other Chirurgions, and God cured him, and is at this day living, God be thanked. The

The hurt of Monsieur *de Pienne*, trepand and cured.

Emperour caused battery to be made with forty double Cannons, where they spared no pouder night nor day. Presently when Monsieur *de Guise* saw the Artillery seated to make a breach, hee made the nearest houses to be pulled downe to make Ramparts, and the posts and beames were ranged, end to end, and betweene two clods of earth, beds and packs of wooll, and then other posts and beames were put againe upon them as before. Now much wood of the houses of the suburbs which had beene put to the ground (for feare least the enemie should be lodged, close covered, and that they should not helpe themselves with any wood) served well to repaire the breach. Every one was busied to carry earth to make the Ramparts night and day. *Messieurs* the Princes, Lords and Captaines, Lieutenants, Ensignes, did all carry the basket, to give example to the Souldiers, and Cittizens to doe the like, which they did; yea both Ladies and Gentlewomen, and those which had not baskets, helpt themselves with kettles, panniers, sackes, sheets, and with what else they could to carry earth; in so much that the enemy had no sooner beaten downe the wall, but hee found behind a Rampart more strong. The wall being fallen our Souldiers cryed to those without, the Fox, the Fox, the Fox, and spake a thousand injuries one to another. Monsieur *de Guise* commanded upon paine of death that no man should speake to them without, for feare least there should be some Traitor who would give them intelligence what was done in the Citty; the command made, they tyed living Cats at the end of their Pikes, and put them upon the Wall and cryed with the Cats miau, miau.

(margin: Princes carried the Baskets.)

Truely the Emperialists were very much vexed to have beene so long making a breach, and at so great expence, which was the breach of fourescore steps, to enter fifty men in front, where they found a Rampart more strong than the wall; they fell upon the poore Catts, and shot at them with their muskets as they use to doe at birds. Our people did oftentimes make sallies by the command of Monsieur *de Guise*. The day before there was a great presse, to make

(margin: Breach.)

themselves enrowled, who must make the sally chiefely
of the young Nobility, led by well experimented Captaines. Insomuch that it was a great favour, to permit them
to sally forth, and runne upon the enemy: and they sallied
forth alwayes the number of one hundred, or sixescore
armed men with Cutlasses, Muskets, Pistolls, Pikes, Parti-
sans and Halberds, which went even to their trenches to
awaken them. Where they presently made an alarum
throughout all their Campe, and their Drummes sounded,
plan, plan, ta, ti, ta, ta, ta, ti, ta, tou, touf, touf: likewise
their Trumpets and Cornets, sounded, to the saddle, to the
saddle, to the saddle, to horse, to horse, to horse, to the
saddle, to horse. And all their souldiers cry'd Arme, arme,
arme, to armes, to armes, to armes, arme, to armes, arme,
to armes, like the cry after Wolves, and all divers tongues,
according to their nations: and they were seene to goe out
from their tents, and little lodgings, as thicke as little Bees,
when their Hive is discovered; to succour their fellowes,
who had their throates cut like sheepe. The horsemen likewise came from all parts, a great gallop, patati, patata,
patati, patapa, ta, ta, patata, patata, and tarried well that
they might not bee in the throng, where stroakes were
imparted to give and receive. And when our men saw they
were forced, they returned into the Citty, still fighting,
and those who runne after were beaten backe with the
Artillery which they had charged with flint stones, and
foure-square peeces of iron; and our souldiers who were
upon the sayd wall made a volley of shot, and showred
downe their bullets upon them like haile, to send them backe
to their lodging, where divers remained in the place of the
combate, and also our men did not all come with whole
skinnes, and there still remained some for the Tythe, who
were joyfull to dye in the bed of honour. And where there
was a horse hurt he was flayed, and eaten by the Souldiers
in steed of beefe and bacon, and it was fit I must runne, to
dresse our hurt men. A few dayes after, other sallyes were
made, which did much anger the enemies, because they

did not let them sleepe but little in safety. Monsieur *de Guise*, made a warlike stratagem which was, he sent a Pesant who was none of the wisest with two paire of Letters toward the King, to whom he gave ten Crownes, and promised the King should give him an hundred, provided he gave him the letters. In the one he sent word that the enemy made no signe of retiring himselfe, and by all force made a great breach which he hop't to defend, yea to the losing of his life, and of all those that were within, and that the enemy had so well placed his Artillery in a certaine place which he named, that with great difficulty was it kept that they had not entred into it, seeing it was a place the most weake of all the Citty: but he hoped quickely to fill it up againe in such sort, that they cannot be able to enter. One of these letters was sowed in the lining of his doublet, and he was bid to take heede that he told it not to any man. And there was also another given to him: wherein the sayd Monsieur *de Guise* sent word to the King, that he & all the beseiged did hope well to keepe the Citty, and other matters, which I cease to speake of. They made the Pesant goe forth in the night, and presently after, he was taken by one that stood Sentinell, and carryed to the Duke of *Alba*, to understand what was done in the Citty, and they asked him if he had any letters, he sayd yes, and gave them one; and having seene it he was put to his oath, whether he had any other, and he swore, not; then they felt and search't him, and found that which was sowed to his doublet, and the poore messenger was hanged.

The sayd letters were communicated to the Emperor, who caused his counsell to be called there, where it was resolved since they could doe nothing at the first breach, that presently the Artillery should be drawne to the place which they thought the most weake, where they made great attempts to make another breach, and dig'd and undermined the wall, and endeavoured to take the Tower of Hell, yet they durst not come to the assault. The Duke of *Alba* declared to the Emperor that the souldiers dyed dayly, yet, more than the number of two hundred, and that there was but little hope to enter into the Citty, seeing the season, and the great quantity of souldiers that there were. The Emperor demanded what people they were that dyed, and if that they were gentlemen of remarke or quality: answeare was made, that they were all poore souldiers; then sayd he, it makes no matter if they dye, comparing them to cater-pillers and grashoppers, which eate the buddes of the earth: And if they were of any fashion, they would not bee in the campe for twelve shillings the month, and therefore no great harme if they dyed. Moreover he sayd he would never part from before that Citty, till he had taken it by force, or famine; although he should loose all his army: by reason of the great number of Princes which were therein, with the most part of the Nobility of *France*. From whom hee hoped to draw double his expence, and that he would goe once againe to *Paris*, to visite the Parisiens, and make himselfe King of all the kingdome of *France*. Monsieur *de Guise* with the Princes, Captaines, and Souldiers, and generally all the Cittizens of the Citty, having understood the intention of the Emperor, which was to extirpate us all, they advised of all they had to doe: And since it was not permitted to the souldiers, nor Cittizens, no nor to the Princes, nor Lords themselves to eate either fresh fish, or Venison, as likewise some Partridges, Woodcockes, Larkes, Plovers, for feare least they had gathered some pestilentiall ayre which might give us any contagion; but that they should content themselves with the ammunition fare, that is to say, with Bisquite, Beefe, poudered Cowes, Lard, and gammons of Bacon: Likewise fish, as Greenefish, Salmon, Sturgeon, Anchovies, Pilchers and Herrings, also Pease, Beanes, Rise, Garlike, Onions, Prunes, Cheese, Butter, Oyle, Salt, Pepper, Ginger, Nutmegges, and other Spiceries to put into pyes, cheefely to horseflesh, which without that would have had a very ill taste; divers Citizens having gardens in the Citty sowed therein great Raddishes, Tur-nippes, Carrots, and Leekes, which they kept well and full deare, against the extremity of hunger. Now all these ammunition victualls were distributed by weight, measure, and justice, according to the quality of the person, because we knew not how long the seige would last. For having understood from the mouth of the Emperor, that he would never part from before *Metz*, till he had taken it by force, or famine; the victualls were lessened, for that which was wont to be distributed to three, was now shared amongst foure, and defence made they should not sell what remained after their dinner, but twas permitted to give it to the wenches that followed the Campe. And rose alwayes from table with an appetite, for feare they should be subject to take Physicke. And before we would yeeld our selves to the mercy of our enemies; had resolved to eate our Asses, Mules, Horses, Dogges, Cats, and Ratts, yea our bootes and other skinnes which we could soften and frie. All the beseiged did generally resolve to defend themselves with all sorts of instruments of warre, that is to say, to ranke, and charge the Artillery, at the entry of the breach with bullets, stones, Cart nayles, barres, and chaines of iron. Also all kinds and differences of artificiall fire; as Boëttes, Bariquadoes, Granadoes, Potts, Lances, torches, squibbes, burning faggots. Moreover scalding water, melted lead, powder of unquenched lime to blind their eyes. Also they were resolved to have made holes through, and through their houses, there to lodge musketiers, there to batter in the flanke and hasten them to goe, or else make them lye for altogether. Also there was order given to the women to unpave the streetes, and to cast them out at their windowes, billets, tables, tressles, formes, and stooles, which would have troubled their braines: moreover there was a little further, a strong Court of Guard, fild with carts and pallisadoes, pipes and hogs heads, fild with earth, for barriquadoes to serve to interlay with faulcons, faulconets, field peeces, harquibuzes, muskets, and pistolls and wilde fire, which would have broken legges and thighes, insomuch that they had beene beaten in head, in flancke, and in tayle; and where they had forced this Court of Guard, there was others at the crossing of the streets, each distant an hundred paces, who have beene as bad companions as the first, and would not have been without making a great many Widdowes, and Orphans. And if fortune would have beene so much against us, as to have broken our Courts of Guard, there was yet seaven great Batallions ordered in square, and triangle, to combate altogether, each one accompanied with a Prince to give them boldnesse, and encourage them to fight, even till the last gaspe, and to dye altogether. Moreover it was resolved, that each one should carry his treasure, rings, and jewells, and their household stuffe of the best, to burne them in the great place, and to put them into ashes rather than the enemy should prevaile and make tropheyes of their spoyles; likewise there was people appointed to put fire to the munition, and to beate out the heads of the Wine caskes, others to put the fire in each house, to burne our enemies and us together: the Citizens had accorded it thus, rather than to see the bloody knife upon their throate, and their Wives and Daughters violated, and to be taken by force, by the cruell and inhumane *Spaniards.* Now we had certaine prisoners which Monsieur *de Guise* sent away upon their faith, to whom was secretly imparted our last resolution, will and desperate mindes; who being arrived in their Campe, doe not deferre the publishing; which bridled the great impetuosity, and will of the souldiers to enter any more into the Citty to cut our throates, and to enrich themselves of our pillage. The Emperor having understood this deliberation of the great warriour, the Duke of *Guise,* put water in his wine, and restrained his great choller and furie, saying, He could not enter into the Citty without making a great slaughter, and butchery, and spill much blood, aswell of the defendants, as of the assaillants, and that they should be dead together, and in the end could have nothing else but a few ashes, and that afterward it might be spoken of that, as of the destruction of *Jerusalem* already made by *Titus* and *Vespasian.* The Emperor then having understood our last resolution, and seeing their little prevailing by their battery, and undermining, and the great plague which was in his whole army, and the indisposition of the time; and the want of victualls and money, and that his souldiers forsooke him, and went away in great companies; concluded in the end to retire themselves accompanied with the Cavallery of his Vantgard, with the greatest part of his Artillery, and the Battalia; The Marquesse of *Brandeborg* was the last which uncampt, maintained by certaine bands of *Spaniards*, *Bohemians*, and his *Germane* companies, and there remained one day and a halfe after, to the great greefe of Monsieur *de Guise*, who caused foure peeces of Artillery to be brought out of the Citty, which he caused to be discharged at him on one side; and the other to hasten them to be gone, which he did full quickely, with all his Troopes. He being a quarter of a league from *Metz* was taken with a feare least our Cavallery should fall upon him in the Rere, which caused him to put fire to his munition powder, and leave certain peeces of Artillery and much baggage which hee could not carry because the Vantgard, and the Battalia, and great Cannons had too much broken the way. Our horsemen would by all meanes have gone out of the Citty to have fallen upon their breech. But Monsieur *de Guise* would never permit them, but on the contrary we should rather make plaine their way, and make them bridges of gold and silver, and let them goe, being like to a good shepheard, who will not loose one of his sheepe. See now how our wellbeloved Imperialists went away from before the Citty of *Metz*, which was the day after *Christmas* day, to the great contentment of the beseiged, and honour of Princes, Captaines and Souldiers who had endured the travells of this seige the space of two monthes. Notwithstanding they did not all goe, there wanted twenty thousand who were dead aswell by Artillery, by the sword, as also by the plague, cold, and hunger, and for spight they could not enter into the Citty to cut our throates, and have the pillage: and also a great number of their horses dyed, of

which they had eaten a great part in steed of Beefe and
Bacon. They went where they had beene encamped, where
they found divers dead bodyes not yet buried, and the
earth all digged like Saint *Innocents* Churchyard, in the
time of the plague. They did likewise leave in their lodgings, pavillions and tents, divers sick people: also bullets,
armes, Carts, Waggons, & other baggage with a great
many of Munition loaves spoyled and rotten by the raine
and snow, yet the souldiers had it not but by weight and
measure; & likewise they left great provision of wood, of
the remainders of the houses of the Villages which they
had pluckt downe 2 or 3 miles compasse, likewise divers
other houses of pleasure belonging to the Citizens accompanied with faire gardens, grasse plotts fild with fruite
trees, for without that they had beene sterv'd with cold,
and had been constrained to have rais'd the seige sooner.
The sayd Monsieur *de Guise* caused the dead to be buried,
and dresse their sicke people: likewise the enemies left in
the Abby of S. *Arnoul* divers of their hurt souldiers which
they could not leade with them: the sayd Monsieur *de Guise*
sent them all Victualls enough, and commanded me and
other Chirurgions to goe dresse them and give them medicines; which we willingly did, and thinke they would not
have done the like toward others (because the *Spaniard* is
most cruell, perfidious and inhumane, & therefore enimy to
all nations) which is proved by *Lopez* a *Spaniard* & *Benzoni*
of *Milan* & others who have written the history of *America*,
& the West *Indies*, who have been constrayned to confesse,
that the cruelty, avarice, blasphemy, and wickednesse of
the *Spaniards*, have altogether alienated the poore *Indians*,
from the religion which the sayd *Spaniards* are sayd to hold.
And all write they are lesse worth than the Idolatrous
Indians, by the cruell usage done to the sayd *Indians*.

And a few dayes after we sent a Trompet to *Thionville*
toward the enemy, that they should send backe for their
wounded men in safety, which they did with Carts and
Waggons, but not enough. Monsieur *de Guise*, caused them

to have Carts and Carters, to helpe to carry them to the
sayd *Thionville*. Our sayd Carters being returned backe,
brought us word that the way was paved with dead bodyes,
and that they never lead backe the halfe, for they dyed in
their Carts, and the *Spaniards* seeing them at the point of
death, before they had cast out their last gaspe, cast them
out of their Carts, and buryed them in the mudde, and
mire, saying they had no order to bring backe the dead.
Moreover our sayd Carters sayd, they met by the way
divers Carts loaden with baggage sticking in the mire,
which they durst not send for backe, for feare least those of
Metz should fall upon them. I will againe returne to the
cause of their mortality, which was principally through
honger, plague, and cold; for the snow was two foote
thicke upon the earth, and they were lodged in the caves
of the earth, onely covered with a little straw. Notwithstanding each souldier had his field bed, and a covering
strewed with glittering starres, more bright than fine gold,
and every day had white sheetes, and lodg'd at the signe of
the Moone, and made good cheere when they had it, and
payd their hoste so well over night, that in the morning
they went away quitte, shaking their eares, and they needed
no combe, to take away the doune out of their haires, either
of head or beard, and found alwayes a white table cloath,
losing good meales for want of Victualls. Also the greatest
part of them had neither bootes, nor buskinnes, slippers,
hose, or shooes, and divers had rather have none than have
them, because they were alwayes in mudde, halfe way of
the legge; and because they went bare leg'd, we called them
the Emperors Apostles. After the Campe was wholly
broaken, I distributed my patients into the hands of the
Chirurgions of the Citty, to finish their cure: then I tooke
leave of Monsieur *de Guise*, and came backe toward the
King, who received me with a loving countenance, and
demanded of me how I did enter into the Citty of *Metz*. I
recounted to him, all that I had done, he caused two
hundred crownes to be given me, and one hundred I had

at my going out, and told me he would not leave me poore; then I thanked him most humbly of the good and the honour which he pleased to doe me.

The Voyage of Hedin, 1553.

Charles the Emperor caused the Citty of *Therouenne* to be beseiged, where Monsieur the Duke of *Savoy*, was Generall of the whole army: it was taken by assault where there was a great number of our men slaine and prisoners. The King willing to prevent that the enemy should not also come to beseige the Citty & Castle of *Hedin*, sent *Messieurs* the Duke *Bouillion*, the Duke *Horace*, the Marquesse of *Villars*, a number of Captaines, and about eight hundred souldiers, & during the seige of *Therouenne*, the sayd Lords fortified the sayd Castle of *Hedin*, in such sort that it seemed impregnable. The King sent me to the sayd Lords to helpe them with my Art, if there were any neede. Now soone after the taking of *Therouenne*, we were beseiged with the army: there was a quicke cleare fountaine or Spring, within Cannon shot, where there was about foure-score whores, and wenches of the enemies, who were round about it to draw water. I was upon a Rampart beholding the Campe, and seeing so many idlers about the sayd fountaine, I prayed Monsieur *de Pont* Commissary of the Artillery, to make one Cannon shot, at that roguish company, he made me much deniall, answearing me that such kind of people were not worth the powder they should waste. Againe I prayed him to levell the Cannon, telling of him, the more dead the fewer enemies; which he did through my request, and at that shot fifteene or six-teene were kild and many hurt. Our souldiers sallied forth upon the enemies, where there was many kild, and slaine with musket shot and swords, as well on the one side, as of the other, and our soldiers did often make sallyes forth upon the enemies before their trenches were made; where I had much worke cut out, so that I had no rest night nor day for dressing the wounded. And I will tell this by the way, that we had put many of them in a great Tower, layd upon a little straw, and their pillowes were stones, their coverlets were their cloakes, of those that had any. Whilst the battery was making, as many shot as the Cannons made, the patients sayd they felt paine in their woundes, as if one had given them blowes with a staffe, the one cry'd his head, the other his arme, and so of other parts; divers of their wounds bled afresh yea in greater quantity than first when they were wounded, and then it was I must runne to stay their bleeding. My little master, if you had beene there, you had beene much troubled with your hot irons, you had neede to have had much charcoale to make them red hot, and beleeve they would have slaine you like a Calfe for this cruelty. Now through this diabolicall tempest of the Eccho from these thundring Instruments, and by the great and vehement agitation of the collision of the ayre resounding and reverberating in the wounds of the hurt people, divers dyed, and others because they could not rest by reason of the groanes and cryes that they made, night and day; and also for want of good nourishment and other good usage necessary to wounded people. Now my little master, if you had beene there, you would hardly have given them gelly, restauratives, cullises,[1] pressures, panada,[2] cleansed barly, white meate, almond milke, Prunes, Raisons, and other proper meates for sicke people: your ordinance would onely have beene accomplisht in paper, but in effect they could have had nothing but old Cow beefe, which was taken about *Hedin* for our munition, salted and halfe boyled, insomuch that who would have eate it he must pull it with the force of his teeth, as birds of Prey doe carrion. I will not forget their linnen wherewith they were drest, which was onely rewashed every day, and dryed at the fire, and therefore dry & stubborne like Parchment, I leave you to thinke how their wounds could heale well. There was foure lusty whores to whom charg was given to wash their linnen, who

[1] i.e. broth.
[2] i.e. a dish of boiled bread with flavourings.

discharged their duty under penalty of the batoone,[1] and also they wanted both soape and water. See then how the sicke people dyed for want of nourishments, and other necessary things. One day our enemies fained to give us a generall assault, to draw our Souldiers upon the breach, to the end to know our countenance and behaviour: every one ranne thither, we had made great provision of artificiall fire, to defend the breach; a Priest belonging to Monsieur *du Bouillon* tooke a granado, thinking to throw it on the enemies, and set it on fire sooner then he ought to have done: it brake asunder, and the fire fell amongst our fire workes, which were put into a house neere the breach; which was to us a mervelous disastre, because it burned diverse poore souldiers: it also tooke hold on the house it-selfe, and we had beene all burned had not great helpe beene used for to quench it; there was but one Well there wherein was water in our Castle, which was almost quite dryed up, and in steede of water, we tooke beere and quenched it: then afterwards we had great scarcity of water; and to drinke the rest that remained which we must straine through napkins.

Now the enemy seeing this smoake and tempest of the fire workes which cast a very great flame and clashing noyse, beleeved wee had put the fire on purpose for the defence of our breach, to burne them, and that wee had great store of others. That made them to be of another opinion, than to take us by assault; they did undermine, and digge into the greatest part of our walls, so that it was the way to overthrow wholly the Castle topsie turvie, and when the mines were finisht, and that their Artillery shot, the whole Castle did shake under us, like an earthquake, which did much astonish us. Moreover he had levelled five peeces of Artillery which they had seated upon a little hill, to play upon our backes when wee should goe to defend the breach.

The Duke *Horace* had a Cannon shot upon one shoulder,

[1] i.e. the baton, or stick.

which caried away his arme on one side, and the body on the other, without being able to speake one onely word. His death was to us a great disasture for the ranke which hee held in this place.

Likewise Monsieur *de Martigues* had a stroake with a Bullet which peirc't through his Lungs; I drest him, as I will declare hereafter. Then we demanded Parle, and a Trumpet was sent toward the Prince of *Piedmont*, to know what composition it pleased him to make us: His answer was, that all the chiefe, as Gentlemen, Captaines, Lieutenants, and Ensignes, should be taken for ransome, and the Souldiers should goe out without Armes; and if they refused this faire and honest proffer, the next day we ought to be assured they would have us by assault or otherwise. Counsell was held, where I was called to know if I would signe as divers Captaines, Gentlemen and others, that the place should bee rendred up. I made answer it was not possible to be held, and that I would signe it with my proper blood, for the little hope that I had, that wee could resist the enemies force, and also for the great desire which I had to be out of this torment, and hell; for I slept not eyther night or day, by reason of the great number of hurt people, which were about two hundred. The dead bodies yeelded a great putrifaction, being heaped one upon the other like Fagots, and not being covered with earth because we had it not; and when I entred into one lodging, Souldiers attended me at the dore to goe dresse others at another; when I went forth, there was striving who should have me, and they carried me like a holy body not touching the ground with my foote in spight one of another, nor could I satisfie so great a number of hurt people. Moreover I had not what was necessary to dresse them withall; for it is not sufficient that the Chirurgion doe his duty towards the patients, but the patient must also doe his, and the assistance, and all exterior things; witnesse *Hippocrates* in his first *Aphorisme*. Now having understood the resolution of the yeelding up of our place, I knew our affaires went not well; and for feare of being knowne I gave a veluet Coate, a Satin doublet, a very fine cloth cloak lin'd with velvet, to a Souldier, who gave me a scurvy old torne doublet cut and slasht with using, and a leather jerkin well examined, and an ill favoured hat, and a little cloake; I smurcht the collar of my shirt with water in which I had mingled a little soote; likewise I wore out my stockings with a stone at the knees and the heeles as if they had beene worne a long time, and I did as much to my shooes, in so much that they would rather take me for a Chimney sweeper, than a Kings Chirurgion. I went in this equipage towards Monsieur *de Martigues*, where I prayd him that he would take order that I might remaine neare him to dresse him, which he agreed to most willingly, and had as much desire I should remaine with him as I my selfe. Soone after, the Commissioners who had charge to elect the prisoners, entred into the Castle, the seaventeenth day of *July* one thousand five hundred fifty three, where they made *Messieurs* the Duke of *Bouillon*, the Marquesse of *Villars*, the Baron of *Culan*, Monsieur *du Pont* commissary of the Artillery, and Monsieur *de Martigues* and I to be taken through the request that he made to them; and all other Gentlemen which they could perceive were able to pay any ransome, and the most part of the Souldiers and the cheefe of the Companies, having such, and so many prisoners as they would.

Afterward the *Spanish* Souldiers entred by the Breach without any resistance, for ours esteemed they would hold their faith and composition that they should have their lives saved. They entred in with a great fury to kill, pillage, and rifle all they retained: some hoping to have ransome, they tyed their stones with Arquebuse cords, which was cast over a Pike which two held upon their shoulders, then pulled the said cord with a great violence and derision, as if they would ring a Bell, telling them that they must put themselves to the ransome, and tell of what houses they were; and if they saw they could have no profit, made them cruelly dye betweene their hands, or presently after their genitall parts would have falne into a Gangreene, and totall mortification; but they kild them all with their Daggers, and cut their throats. See now their great cruelty and perfidiousnesse, let him trust to it that will. Now to returne to my purpose being lead from the Castle to the Citty with Monsieur *de Martigues*, there was a Gentleman of the Duke of *Savoyes*, who asked mee if Monsieur *de Martigues* wound was curable, I answered, not; who presently went and told the Duke of *Savoy*; now I thought he would send Physitions and Chirurgions to visit and dresse my said Monsieur *de Martigues*: in the meane time I thought with my selfe whether I ought to make it nice and not to acknowledge my selfe a Chirurgion for feare least they should retaine mee to dresse their wounded, and in the end they would know I was the Kings Chirurgion, and that they would make me pay a great ransome. On the other side I feared, if I should not make my selfe knowne to bee a Chirurgion, and to have carefully dressed Monsieur *de Martigues*, they would cut my throate, so that I tooke a resolution to make it appeare to them he would not dye for want of good dressing and looking to. Soone after, see, there arrives divers gentlemen accompanied with the Physition and Chirurgion to the Emperour, and those of the said Duke of *Savoy*, with sixe other Chirurgions following the Army, to see the hurt of the said Lord of *Martigues*, and to know of mee how I had dressed him, and with what medicines. The Emperours Physition bid me declare the essence of the wound, and how I had drest it. Now all the assistants had a very attentive eare to know if the wound were mortall or not: I began to make a discourse that Monsieur *de Martigues* looking over the wall to perceive them that did undermine it, received a shot from an Arquebuse quite through the body; presently I was called to dresse him, I saw hee cast blood out of his mouth, and his wounds. Moreover he had a great difficultie of breathing, and cast out winde by the said wounds with a

whistling, in so much that it would blow out a Candle, and
he said he had a most sharpe pricking paine at the entrance
of the Bullet. I doe beleeve and thinke it might bee some
little peeces of bones which prickt the Lungs. When they
made their Systole and Diastole, I put my finger into him;
where I found the entrance of the Bullet to have broken
the fourth Rib in the middle and scales of bones which the
said Bullet had thrust in, and the outgoing of it had likewise
broken the fift Rib with peeces of bones which had beene
driven from within outward; I drew out some but not all,
because they were very deepe and adherent. I put in each
wound a Tent, having the head very large, tyed with a
thread, least by the inspiration it might bee drawne into
the capacity of the *Thorax*, which hath beene knowne by
experience to the detriment of the poore wounded; for
being fallen in, it cannot be taken out, which is the cause
that engenders putrifaction, a thing contrary to nature.
The said Tents were annointed with a medicine compos'd
of yolks of Egges, *Venice* Turpentine, with a little oyle of
Roses: My intention for putting the Tents was to stay the
flux of blood, and to hinder that the outward ayre did not
enter into the breast, which might have cooled the Lungs
and by consequent the heart. The said Tents were also put,
to the end that issue might bee given for the blood that
was spilt within the *Thorax*. I put upon the wound great
Emplasters of *Diacalcitheos*[1] in which I had relented oyle of
Roses and Vinigar to the avoyding of inflammation, then
I put great stupes of *Oxycrate*,[2] and bound him up, but not
hard, to the end he might have easie respiration; that done
I drew from him five porrengers of blood from the
Basilicke veine of the right arme, to the end to make
revulsion of the blood which runs from the wounds into
the *Thorax*, having first taken indication from the wounded
part, and cheefely his forces, considering his youth and his

---

[1] i.e. diachylon plaster, an astringent application of oil, litharge, and
vitriol.
[2] A mixture, chiefly vinegar and saffron.

sanguine temper; Hee presently after went to stoole, and
by his urine and seege cast great quantity of blood. And as
for the paine which he said he felt at the entrance of the
Bullet which was as if he had been pricked with a bodkin,
that was because the Lungs by their motion beate against
the splinters of the broken Rib. Now the Lungs are covered
with a coate comming from the membrane called *Pleura*,
interweaved with nerves of the sixt conjugation from the
braine, which was cause of the extreame paine he felt;
likewise he had a great difficultie of breathing, which proceeded from the blood which was spilt in the capacitie of
the *Thorax*, and upon the *Diaphragme*, the principall instrument of respiration, and from the dilaceration of the muscles
which are betweene each Rib, which helpe also to make the
expiration and the inspiration; and likewise because the
Lungs were torne and wounded by the Bullet, which hath
caused him ever since to spit blacke and putrid blood in
coughing. The Feaver seazed him soone after he was hurt,
with faintings and swoonings. It seemed to mee that the
said feaver proceeded from the putredinous vapours arising
from the blood which is out of his proper vessells, which
hath fallen downe, and will yet flow downe. The wound of
the Lungs is growne great and will grow more great,
because it is in perpetuall motion, both sleeping and
waking, and is dilated and comprest to let in the aire to the
heart, and cast fuliginous vapours out: by the unnaturall
heate is made inflammation, then the expulsive vertue is
constrained to cast out by cough whatsoever is obnoxious
unto it: for the Lungs cannot be purged but by coughing,
& by coughing the wound is dilated, and growes greater,
from whence the blood issues out in great aboundance,
which blood is drawne from the heart by the veine arteriall
to give them nourishment, and to the heart by the *vena
cava*; his meate was barly broth, stewed prunes, sometimes
panada; his drinke was Ptisan: He could not lye but upon
his backe which shewed he had a great quantity of blood
spilt within the capacity of the *Thorax*, and being spread or

spilled along the spondills, doth not so much presse the Lungs as it doth being laid on the sides or sitting.

What shall I say more, but that the said Lord *Martigues* since the time hee was hurt hath not reposed one houre onely, and hath alwayes cast out bloody urines and stooles. These things then *Messieurs* considered, one can make no other prognosticke but that he will dye in a few dayes, which is to my great greefe. Having ended my discourse I drest him as I was wont; having discovered his wounds, the Physitions and other assistants presently knew the truth of what I had said.

The said Physitions having felt his pulse and knowne his forces to be almost spent, and abolished, concluded with mee that in a few dayes he would dye; and at the same instant went all toward the Lord of *Savoy*, where they all said, that the said Lord *Martigues* would dye in a short time; he answered, it were possible if hee were well drest he might escape. Then they all with one voyce said, hee had beene very well drest, and sollicited with all things necessary for the curing of his wounds, and could not be better, and that it was impossible to cure him, and that his wound was mortall of necessity. The Monsieur *de Savoy* shewed himselfe to bee very much discontented and wept, and asked them againe if for certaine they all held him deplored and remedilesse, they all answered, yes. Then a certaine *Spanish* impostor offered himselfe who promised on his life that he would cure him, and if he failed to cure him, they should cut him in an hundred peeces; but he would not have any Physitions, Chirurgions or Apothecaries with him. And at the same instant the sayd Lord of *Savoy* told the Physitions and Chirurgions they should not in any wise goe any more to see the sayd Lord of *Martigues.* Also he sent a Gentleman to me to forbid me upon paine of life not to touch any more the said Lord of *Martigues,* which I promised not to doe; wherefore I was very glad, seeing he should not dye in my hands, and commanded the said impostor to dresse the said Lord of *Martigues.* And that he should have no other Physitions nor Chirurgions but him; he came presently to the said Lord of *Martigues*, who told him,

Senor Cavallero el senor Duque mé ha mandado que viniesse a curar vostra herida, yo os jura á Dios que antes de ocho dias yo os haga subir a Cavallo con la lansa, en puno con tal que no ayo que yo qu'os toque. Comereis y bibereis todas comidas que fueren de vostro gusto y yo hare la dieta pro V. m. y desto os de veis aseguirar sobre de mi, yo he sanado munchos que tenian mayores heridas que la Vostra. That is to say, Lord *Cavalleere*, Monsieur the Duke of *Savoy* hath commanded me to come dresse thy wound; I sweare to thee by God, that before eight dayes I will make thee mount on horsebacke with thy Lance in thy hand, provided, that no man may touch thee but my selfe; thou shalt eate and drinke any thing thou hast a minde to, I will performe thy diet for thee, and of this thou maist be assured upon my promise, I have cured divers who have had greater wounds than thine: and the Lord replyed, God give you the grace to doe it.

He demanded of the sayd Lord a shirt and tore it in little ragges, which hee put a crosse, muttering, and murmuring certaine words over the wound; and having drest him, permitted him to eate and drinke what he would, telling him hee would observe a dyet for him, which he did, eating but six prunes and sixe bits of bread at a meale, and drinking but beere. Notwithstanding, two dayes after, the sayd Lord of *Martigues* dyed; and my *Spaniard*, seeing of him in the agony, eclipst himselfe and got away without bidding farewell to any body; and I beleeve if he had beene taken he had bin hang'd for his false promises, which he had made to Monsieur the Duke of *Savoy*, and to divers other gentlemen.

He dyed about tenne of the clocke in the morning, and after dinner, the sayd Lord of *Savoy*, sent Physitions and Chirurgions and his Apothecary, with a great quantity of Drogues, to embalme him; they came accompanied with divers gentlemen and Captaines of the Army.

The Emperors Chirurgion came neere to me, and prayed me kindly to open the body; which I refused, telling him I was not worthy to carry his plaster boxe after him: he prayed me againe, which then I did for his sake, if it so liked him. I would yet againe have excused my selfe, that seeing he was not willing to embalme him, that he would give this charge to another Chirurgion of the company; he made me yet answere, that he would it should be I, and if I would not doe it, I might hereafter repent it: knowing this his affection, for feare he should not doe me any displeasure, I tooke the rasor and presented it to all in particular, telling them I was not well practised to doe such operations which they all refused.

The body being placed upon a table, truely I purposed to shew them that I was an Anatomist, declaring to them diverse things, which should be heere too long to recite. I began to tell all the company that I was sure the bullet had broken two ribs, and that it had past through the Lungs, and that they should finde the wound much enlarged, because they are in perpetuall motion, sleeping or waking, and by this motion the wound was the more dilacerated. Also that there was great quantity of blood spilt in the capacity of the brest, and upon the midriffe, and splinters of the broken ribbes which were beaten in at the entrance of the bullet, and the issuing forth of it, had carried out. Indeed all which I had told them was found true in the dead body.

One of the Physitions asked me, which way the blood might passe to be cast out by Urine, being contained in the *Thorax*. I answeared him that there was a manifest conduit, which is the *Vena Azygos*, who having nourisht the ribbes, the rest of the blood descends under the *Diaphragme*, and on the left side is conjoyned to the emulgent veine, which is the way by which the matter in *pleuresies* and in *Empiema*, doe manifestly empty themselves by urine and stoole. As it is likewise seene, the pure milke of the brests of women newly brought to bed, to descend by the *Mammillary* Veines, and to be evacuated downewards by the necke of the wombe without being mixt with the blood. And such a thing is done (as it were by a miracle of nature) by her expulsive and sequestering vertue, which is seene by experience of two glasse vessells called Mount-wine; let the one be filled with water, and the other with Claret wine, and let them be put the one upon the other, that is to say, that which shall bee filled with water, upon that which shall be filled with wine; and you shall apparently see the wine mount up to the top of the vessell quite through the water, and the water descend atraverse the wine, and goe to the bottome of the vessell without mixture of both; and if such a thing be done so exteriorly and openly to the sense of our eye, by things without life: you must beleeve the same in our understanding. That nature can make matter and blood to passe, having beene out of their vessells yea through the bones without being mingled with the good blood.

Our discourse ended, I embalmed the body, and put it into a Coffinne; after that the Emperors Chirurgion tooke me apart, and told me if I would remaine with him that he would use me very well, and that he would cloath me anew, also that I should ride on horsebacke. I thanked him very kindly for the honour he did me, and told him that I had no desire to doe service to strangers, and enemies to my Countrey; then he told mee I was a foole, and if he were prisoner as I, hee would serve the divell to get his liberty. In the end I told him flat that I would not dwell at all with him.

The Emperors Physition returned toward the sayd Lord of *Savoy*, where he declared the cause of the death of the sayd Lord of *Martigues*, and told him that it was impossible for all the men in the world to have cured him; and confirmed againe, that I had done what was necessary to be done, and prayed him to winne mee to his service, and spoke better of me than I deserved.

Having beene perswaded to take me to his service, he gave charge to one of his stewards named Monsieur *du*

Bouchet, to tell me, if I would dwell in his service that he would use me kindly: I answered him, that I thank't him most humbly, and that I had resolved not to dwell with any stranger. This my answer being heard by the Duke of *Savoy*, he was somewhat in choller, and sayd, hee would send mee to the Gallies.

Monsieur *de Vaudeville*, Governour of *Graveline*, and Colonell of seaventeene Ensignes of foote, prayed him, to give me to him, to dresse him of an Ulcer which he had in his Leg this six or seaven yeares; Monsieur *de Savoy* told him because I was of worth, that he was content, and if I ranckled his Leg it would be well done; Hee answered that if he perceaved any thing, that hee would cause my throate to be cut.

Soone after, the said Lord of *Vaudeville* sent for me by fowre Germane Halberdiers, which affrighted me much, not knowing whither they led mee, they spake no more *French* than I high *Dutch*; being arrived at his lodging, he told mee I was welcome, and that I was his; and as soone as I should have cured him of that Ulcer in his Leg, that he would give me leave to be gone without taking any ransome of me. I told him I was not able to pay any ransome.

Then he made his Physition and Chirurgions in ordinary to shew mee his ulcerated Leg; having seene and considered it, we went apart into a Chamber where I began to tell them, that the said Ulcer was annuall, not being simple but complicated: that is to say, of a round figure, and scaly, having the lips hard and callous, hollow and sordid, accompanied with a great varicous veine which did perpetually feede it; besides a great tumor, and a phlegmonous distemper very painefull through the whole Leg, in a body of cholericke complexion; as the haire of his face and beard demonstrated. The method to cure it (if cured it could be) was to begin with universall things, that is, with purgation and bleeding, and with this order of dyet, that hee should not use any wine at all, nor any salt meates, or of great nourishment, chiefely these which did heat the blood: after-

ward the cure must be begun with making divers scarifications about the Ulcer, and totally cutting away the callous
edges or lips, and giving a long or a triangular figure, for
the round will very hardly cure, as the Ancients have left
it in writing, which is seene by experience. That done, the
filth must be mundified,[1] as also the corrupted flesh, which
should be done with *Unguentum Ægyptiacum*, and upon it a
bolster dipt in juice of Plantaine and Nightshade and
Oxycrate, and roule the Leg beginning at the foote, and
finishing at the knee, not forgetting a little bolster upon the
Varicous veine, to the end no superfluities should flow to
the Ulcer. Moreover that he should take rest in his bed,
which is commanded by *Hippocrates*, who saith, that those
who have soare Legs should not use much standing or
sitting, but lying along. And after these things done and
the Ulcer well mundified, a plate of Lead rubbed with
quickesilver should be applyed. See then the meanes, by
which the said Lord *Vaudeville* might be cured of the said
Ulcer; all which they found good. Then the Physition left
mee with the Chirurgion, and went to the Lord *Vaudeville*;
to tell him that he did assure him I would cure him, and
told him all that I had resolved to doe, for the cure of his
Ulcer: whereof hee was very joyfull. He made mee to bee
called to him, and asked me if I was of the opinion that his
Ulcer could be cured, and I told him, yes, provided he
would be obedient to doe what he ought. He made me a
promise hee would performe all things which I would
appoint; and as soone as his Ulcer should be cured, he
would give me liberty to returne without paying any
ransome. Then I beseech't him to come to a better composition with me, telling him that the time would be too
long to bee in liberty, if I stayd till hee was perfectly well,
and that I hoped within fifteene dayes the Ulcer should bee
diminished more than one halfe, and it should bee without
paine, and that his Physitions and Chirurgions would finish
the rest of the cure very easily. To which hee agreed, and

[1] i.e. cleansed.

then I tooke a peece of paper, and cut it the largenesse of the Ulcer, which I gave him, and kept as much my selfe. I prayd him to keepe promise, when he should finde his businesse done: He swore by the faith of a Gentleman he would doe it; then I resolved to dresse him well, according to the method of *Galen*, which was, that after all strange things were taken out of the Ulcer, and that there wanted nothing but filling up with flesh, I drest him but once a day, and he found that very strange. And likewise his physition which was but a fresh man in those affaires, who would perswade mee with the Patient, to dresse him two or three times a day, I prayd him to let me doe what I thought good; and that it was not to prolong the cure, but on the contrary, to hasten it, for the great desire I had to be in liberty. And that he would looke in *Galen* in the fourth book of the composition of medicaments *secundum genera*, who saith, that if a medicine doe not remaine long upon the part it profits not so much, as when it doth continue long, a thing which many Physitions have been ignorant of, and have thought it hath beene better to change the Plaster often. And this ill custome is so inveterate and rooted, that the Patients themselves accuse oftentimes the Chirurgions of negligence, because they doe not oftner remove their emplasters; but they are deceived. For as you have understood and read in my workes in divers places: The qualities of all bodies which mutually touch, operate one against another, and both of them suffer something, where one of them is much stronger than the other, by meanes whereof the said qualities are united, they familiarise with the time, although they are very much differing from the manner, that the quality of the medicament doth unite, and sometimes becomes like to that of the body, which is a very profitable thing. Therefore they say, he is to be praised much who first invented not to change the Plasters so often, because it is knowne by experience, this is a good invention.

Moreover it is said, great fault is committed to dresse

Ulcers often in wiping of them hard, for one takes not
away onely the unprofitable excrement, which is the *pus* or
Sanies of the Ulcer, but the matter whereof the flesh is
engendred; wherefore for the reasons aforesaid it is not
needefull to dresse Ulcers so often.

The said Lord *Vaudeville*, would see whether that which
I alledged out of *Galen* were true, and commanded the said
Physition to looke there, for that hee would know it; he
caused the booke to be brought upon the table, where my
saying was found true, and then the Physition was ashamed,
and I very joyfull. So that the said Lord of *Vaudeville*
desired not to bee dressed but once a day, in so much that
within fifteene dayes the Ulcer was almost cicatrized; the
composition being made betweene us, I began to be merry.
He made me eate and drinke at his Table, when there was
not men of more great ranke with him.

He gave me a great red scarfe, which hee commanded
me to weare. I may say I was as glad of it as a dog that hath
a clog, for feare he should goe into the vineyard and eate
the grapes. The Physition and Chirurgion led mee through
the Campe to visit their hurt people, where I tooke notice
what our enemies did; I perceived they had no more
peeces of Cannon, but onely twenty five or thirty peeces
for the field.

Monsieur *de Vaudeville* held Monsieur *de Bauge* prisoner,
the brother of Monsieur *de Martigues* who dyed at *Hedin*.
The said Lord of *Bauge* was prisoner in the Castle of the
heape of wood belonging to the Emperour, who had beene
taken at *Therouenne* by two *Spanish* Souldiers. Now the
said Lord of *Vaudeville* having looked well upon him, conceived he must be a Gentleman of some good house, and
to be the better assured, he caused him to have his stockings
pulled off, & seeing his stockings and his feete cleane and
neate, together with his white fine socke, it confirmed him
the better in his opinion, that it was a man was able to pay
some good ransome. He demands of the Souldiers if they
would take thirty Crownes for their prisoner, and that he

would give it to them presently, to which they agreed
willingly, because they had neither meanes to keepe him,
nor feede him; besides they knew not his worth, therefore
they delivered their prisoner into the hands of the said
Lord of *Vaudeville*, who presently sent him to the Castle of
the heape of wood with a guard of foure Souldiers with
other Gentlemen prisoners of ours. The said Lord *Bauge*
would not discover himselfe, who hee was, and endured
very much, being kept but with bread and water, and lay
upon a little straw. The said Lord of *Vaudeville* after the
taking of *Hedin*, sent word to the said Lord *Bauge* and other
prisoners, that the place of *Hedin* was taken, and the list of
those that had beene slaine, and amongst the rest, Monsieur
de Martigues: and when the said Lord of *Bauge* heard the
sound of the death of his brother the Lord *Martigues*, he
began much to weepe and lament; his keeper demanded
of him, why he made so many & so great lamentations?
He declared unto them that it was for Monsieur *de Martigues* his brothers sake. Having understood that, the Captaine of the Castle dispatcht a man away quickly, to tell it
to Monsieur *de Vaudeville* that he had a good prisoner; who
having received this good newes rejoyced greatly, and the
next day sent me with his physition and foure Souldiers to
the wood Castle to know if his prisoner would give him
fifteene thousand Crownes for a ransome; he would send
him free to his owne house, and for the present he desired
but the security of two Merchants of *Antwerp*, that hee
would name. The said Lord *Vaudeville* perswaded me that
I would make his agreement with his prisoner. See then
why he sent me to the woodden Castle, and commanded
the Captaine of the Castle to use him well, and to put him
into a Chamber hung with Tapestrie, and that they should
make his guard more strong, and from that time they made
him good cheare at his expence.

The answer of the said Lord of *Bauge* was, that to put
himselfe to ransome hee was not able; and that, that
depended upon Monsieur *d'Estamps* his Unckle, and of

Mistrisse *de Bressure* his Aunt, and that he had not any meanes to pay such a ransome. I returned with my keepers to the said Lord *Vaudeville*, and told him the answer of his said prisoner, who told me, Perhaps he should not go out at so good a rate, which was true, for he was discovered. And forthwith the Queene of *Hungary*, and the Duke of *Savoy* sent word to the Lord *Vaudeville*, that this morsell was too great for him, and that he must send him to them, (which he did) and that he had enough prisoners besides him: he was put to forty thousand Crownes ransome besides other expenses.

Returning toward the said Lord *Vaudeville* I passed by S. *Omer*, where I saw their great peeces of battery, whereof the greatest part was flawed and broken. I came back also by *Therouenne*, where I did not see so much as stone upon stone, unlesse the marke of a great Church. For the Emperour gave commandement to the country people within five or six leagues about, that they should empty and carry away the stones; in so much, that now one may drive a Cart over the Citty, as is likewise done at *Hedin*, without any appearance of Castle or Fortresse. See then the mischeefe which comes by the warres.

And to returne to my purpose, presently after my said Lord *Vaudeville* was very well of his Ulcer and little wanted of the entire cure, which was the cause hee gave me my leave, and made me be conducted with a Passeport by a Trumpet to *Abbeville*, where I tooke post, and went and found the King *Henry* my Master at *Aufimon*, who received me with joy, and a good countenance.

He sent for the Duke of *Guise* the high Constable of *France*, and Monsieur *d'Estrez*, to understand by me what had past at the taking of *Hedin*; and I made them a faithfull report, and assured them I had seene the great peeces of Battery, which they had carried to S. *Omer*. Whereof the King was very joyfull, because hee feared least the enemy should come further into *France*. He gave me two hundred Crownes to retire my selfe to my owne house, and I was

very glad to bee in liberty and out of this great torment and
noise of Thunder from the Diabolicke artillery, and farre
from the Souldiers, blasphemers and deniers of God. I will
not omit to tell here that after the taking of *Hedin*, the king
was advertised that I was not slaine, but that I was a prisoner,
which his Majestie caused to be written to my wife by
Monsieur *du Goguier* his cheefe Physition, and that shee
should not be in any trouble of mind for me, for that I was
safe and well, and that he would pay my ransome.

The Battell of S. Quintin. 1557.

After the battell of S. *Quintin*, the King sent me to the
Fere in *Tartenois* toward Monsieur the Marshall of *Bourdillon*, to have a Passeport by the Duke of *Savoy* to goe to
dresse Monsieur the Constable, who was grievously hurt
with a Pistoll shot in the backe, whereof hee was like to dye,
and remained a prisoner in his enemies hands. But the
Duke of *Savoy* would never give consent that I should goe
to the said Lord Constable, saying hee should not remaine
without a Chirurgion, and that he doubted I was not sent
onely to dresse him, but to give him some advertisement,
and that he knew I understood something else besides
Chirurgery, and that he knew me to have been his prisoner
at *Hedin*. Monsieur the Marshall of *Bourdillon* advertized
the King of the Dukes deniall, by which meanes the King
writ to the said Lord of *Bourdillon*, that if my Lady, the
Lord high Constables wife, did send any body of her
house; which was an able man, that I should give him a
letter, and that I should also have told him by word of
mouth, what the King and Monsieur the Cardinall of
Lorraine had given me in charge. Two dayes after there
arrives a servant of the Lord Constables Chamber, who
brought him shirts, and other linnen, for which the sayd
Lord Marshall gave Passe-port, to goe to the sayd Lord
Constable; I was very glad thereof, and gave him my letter,
and gave him his lesson, of that which his Master should
doe, being prisoner. I had thought being discharged of my

embassage to returne toward the King. But the sayd Lord
of *Bourdillon* pray'd me to stay with him at the Fere to
dresse a great number of people who were hurt, and were
thither retired after the battell; and that he would send
word to the King, the cause of my stay; which I did. The
wounds of the hurt people were greatly stincking, and full
of wormes with Gangreene and putrifaction; so that I was
constrayned to come to my knife to amputate that which
was spoyld, which was not without cutting off armes and
legges, as also to Trepan diverse. Now there were not any
medicines to be had at the Fere, because the Chirurgions
of our Campe had carried all with them; I found out that
the Chariot of the Artillery tarried behind at the Fere, nor
had it yet beene touched. I prayd the sayd Lord Marshall
that he would cause some of the drogues to be delivered
unto me which were in it; which he did, and there was
given to me, one halfe onely at a time: and five or sixe
dayes after I was constrayned to take the rest, neither was
there halfe enough to dresse so great a number of the
people, and to correct and stay the putrifaction, and to kill
the wormes which were entred into their wounds; I
washed them with *Ægyptiacum* dissolved in wine and *Aqua
vitæ*, and did for them, all which I could possible, yet notwithstanding all my diligence, very many of them dyed.

There were Gentlemen at the Fere who had charge to
finde out the dead body of Monsieur *de Bois-Dolphin* the
elder, who had beene slaine in the battell; they prayed me
to accompany them to the Campe to finde him out
amongst the dead, if it were possible, which indeed was
impossible; seeing that the bodyes were all disfavoured
and overwhelmed with putrefaction. We saw more than
halfe a league about us the earth covered with dead bodyes;
neither could we abide long there, for the cadaverous seents,
which did arise from the dead bodyes, aswell of men, as of
horses. And I thinke we were the cause, that so great a
number of flyes, rose from the dead bodees, which were
procreated by their humidity and the heate of the Sunne,

having their tayles greene and blew; that being up in the ayre made a shaddow in the Sunne. We heard them buzze, or humme, which was much mervaile to us. And I thinke it was enough to cause the Plague, where they alighted. (My little master) I would you had beene there as I was, to distinguish the ordures and also to make report to them which were never there. Now being cloyed and annoyed in that Countrey, I prayd Monsieur the Lord Marshall, to give me my leave to be gone, and that I was affrayd I should be sicke, by reason of my too great paines, and the stinckes which did arise from the wounded bodyes, which did almost all dye, for what diligence soever was used unto them. He made other Chirurgions, to come finish the dressing of the sayd hurt people, and I went away with his good grace and favour. He wrote a letter to the King, of the paines I had taken with the poore wounded. Then I returned to *Paris*, where I found yet many Gentlemen who had beene hurt, and were there retired after the battell.

The Voyage of the Campe of Amiens, 1558.

The King sent me to *Dourlan*, and made me to be conducted by Captaine *Gouast* with fifty men in armes, for feare I should be taken by the enemies. And seeing that in the way we were alwayes in alarums, I caused my man to alight, making him to be my master for that time, and I got upon his horse, which carryed my male,[1] and tooke his cloake and hat, and gave him my ambling Mare. My man being upon her backe, one would have taken him for the master, and I for the servant. Those of *Dourlan* seeing us farre off, thought we were enemies, and let flye their Cannon shot at us. Captaine *Gouast* my conductor, made signe with his hat, that we were not enemies, so that they left shooting, and we entred into *Dourlan* with great joy. Those of *Dourlan* made a sally forth, upon the enemies five or sixe dayes before, who kild and hurt diverse of our Captaines, and good souldiers; and amongst the rest Cap-

[1] i.e. mail, or bag.

taine St. *Aubin* valiant at the sword, whom Monsieur *de Guise* loved very well, and for whom chiefely the King sent me thither, who being in the fit of a quartaine feaver, would needes goe out to command the greatest part of his company: a *Spaniard* seeing him that he commanded, perceived hee was a Captaine, and shot a musket bullet quite through his necke; my Captaine Saint *Aubin* thought with this stroake he was dead, and with the feare (I protest to God) he lost his quartane ague, and was altogether freed from it. I dressed him with *Anthony Portail* Chirurgion in ordinary to the King, and divers other Souldiers: some dyed, others escaped quit with the losse of a legge, or an arme, or the losse of an eye, and they sayd they escaped good cheape, escape that can. When the enemie had broke their Campe, I returned to *Paris*. Heere I hold my peace of my little master, who was more at ease in his house than I at the Warres.

The voyage of Harbor *of Grace,*[1] 1563.

Yet I will not omit to speake of the voyage of the *Harbor* of Grace; then when they made the approaches to plant the Artillery, the English who were within it kild some of our Souldiers, & divers Pioners, who undermined, who when they were seene to be so hurt that there was no hope of curing, their fellowes stript them & put them yet alive, in the mines, which served them for so much filling earth. The *English* seeing they could not withstand an assault, because they were very much attainted with diseases, and chiefely with the Plague, they yeelded, their lives and jewells saved. The King caused them to have shippes to returne to *England*, being glad to be out of this place infected with the Plague: the greatest part dyed, and carryed the Plague into *England*, and since have not yet beene exempted. Captaine *Sarlabous* master of the Campe, was left there in garrison, with sixe Ensignes on foote, who had no feare of the Plague, and were very joyfull to enter

[1] Havre le Grâce.

therein, hoping there to make good cheere. My little
master had you beene there you had done as they.

The Voyage to Rouen, 1562.

Now for the taking of *Rouen* they kild divers of ours
before the assault, and at the assault: the day after they
entred into the Citty, I Trepaned eight or nine, who were
hurt at the breach with the stroakes of stones. There was so
malignant an ayre, that divers dyed, yea of very small hurts,
insomuch that some thought they had poysoned their
bullets: those within sayd the like by us, for although they
were well treated in their necessities within the Citty, yet
they dyed also aswell as those without. The King of *Navar*
was hurt in the shoulder with a bullet some few dayes
before the assault; I visited and helpt to dresse him, with
his owne Chirurgion, named Master *Gilbert* one of the
chiefe of *Montpelier*, and others. They could not finde the
bullet, I searcht for it very exactly, I perceived by conjecture, that it was entred by the head of the *Adiutorium*,[1] and
that it had runne into the cavity of the sayd bone, which
was the cause we could not finde it. The most part of them
sayd it was entred and lost within the cavity of the body.
Monsieur the Prince of the *Rocke-upon-Yon*, who intimately
loved the King of *Navarre*, drew me to one side, and askt
me if the wound was mortall. I told him yea, because all
wounds made in great joynts, and principally contused
wounds, were mortall according to all Authors who have
written of them. He enquired of the others what they
thought, and cheefely of the sayd *Gilbert*, who told him
that hee had great hope that the King his master, would be
cured, and the sayd Prince was very joyfull. Foure dayes
after the King and the Queene mother, Monsieur the
Cardinall of *Bourbon* his brother, Monsieur the Prince of
Rocke-upon-Yon, Monsieur *de Guise*, and other great per-
sonages, after we had dressed the King of *Navarre*, caused
a consultation to be made in their presences, where there

[1] i.e. the humerus.

was diverse Physitions and Chirurgions: each man sayd what seemed good unto him, and there was not one of them, who had not good hope of him; saying that the King would be cured, and I persisted alwayes on the contrary.

Monsieur the Prince of the *Rocke-upon-Yon* who loved me, withdrew me aside, and sayd I was onely against the opinion of all the rest, and prayd me not to be obstinate against so many worthy men. I answered him, that when I saw any good signes of cure, I would change my advise. Divers consultations were made, where I never changed my word, and prognosticke, such as I had made at the first dressing, and alwayes sayd that the arme would fall into a Gangreene, which it did, what diligence soever could be had to the contrary; and gave up his soule to God the eighteenth day of his hurt. Monsieur the Prince *Upon Yon*, having heard of the death of the sayd King, sent his Physition and Chirurgion toward me, named *Fèvre* now in ordinary to the King, and to the Queene Mother, to tell me, that he would have the bullet taken out, and that it should be lookt for in what place so ever it could be found: then I was very joyfull, and told them that I was well assured to finde it quickely, which I did in their presences, and divers gentlemen. It was lodged in the very midst of the cavity of the Adiutory bone. My sayd Prince having it, shewed it to the King and the Queene, who all sayd, my prognosticke was found true. The body was layd to rest in the Castle Galliard, and I returned to *Paris*, where I found divers hurt men who were hurt at the breach at *Rouen*, and cheefely *Italians*, who desired me very much to dresse them, which I did willingly; there were divers that recovered; and others dyed. I beleeve (my little master) you were called to dresse some of them, for the great number there was of them.

The Voyage of the battell of Dreux 1562.

The day after the battell given at *Dreux*, the King commanded me, to goe dresse Monsieur the Count of *Eu*, who had beene hurt with a Pistoll shot in the right thigh, neere the joynt of the hippe; which fractured and broke the *Os femoris* in divers places, from whence divers accidents did arise, and then death, which was to my great greefe. The day after my arrivall I would goe to the field, where the battell was given, to see the dead bodyes; I saw a league about, all the earth covered, where there was by estimation five and twenty thousand men, or more. All which were dispatcht in the space of two houres. I would (my little master) for the love I beare you, that you had beene there to recount it to your schollers and to your children. Now in the meane time while I was at *Dreux* I visited and drest a great number of gentlemen and poore Souldiers, & amongst the rest many *Swisser* Captaines, I dressed 14 in one chamber, onely all hurt with Pistoll shot, and other instruments of Diabolicall fire, and not one of the foureteene dyed. Monsieur the Count of *Eu* being dead, I made no long tarrying at *Dreux*: there came Chirurgions from *Paris* who performed well their duty toward the hurt people, as *Pigray, Cointeret, Hubert,* and others; and I returned to *Paris,* where I found diverse gentlemen wounded, who had retired themselves thither after the battell to be drest of their hurts.

The Voyage of the battell of Moncontour. 1569.

During the battell of *Moncontour* King *Charles* was at *Plessy* the Towers, where he heard they had wonne it; a great number of hurt gentlemen and Souldiers withdrew themselves into the Citty and suburbes of Towers, to be drest and helpt, where the King and Queene Mother commanded me to shew my duty with the other Chirurgions, who were then in quarter, as *Pigray, du Bois, Portail,* and one named *Siret,* a Chirurgion of *Towers,* a man very skilfull in Chirurgery, and at that time Chirurgion to the Kings brother; and for the multitude of the wounded wee were but little in repose, nor the Physitions likewise. Count *Mansfield* Governer of the *Duchy* of *Luxembourge,* Knight of the King of *Spaines* order, was greatly hurt in the battell, in the left arme, with a Pistoll shot, which broke a great part of the joynt of the elbow, and had retired himselfe to *Bourgueil* neere *Towers*; being there he sent a gentlemen to the King, affectionately to beseech him to send one of his Chirurgions to helpe him in his hurt. Counsell was held what Chirurgion should be sent. Monsieur the Marshall of *Montmorency* told the King and the Queene, that it were best to send him his cheefe Chirurgion, and declared to them that the sayd Lord *Mansfield* was one part of the cause of winning the battell. The King sayd flat he would not that I should goe, but would have me remaine close to him. Then the Queene Mother sayd, I should but goe and come, and that he must consider it was a strange Lord, who was come from the King of *Spaines* side, to help and succour him. And upon this he permitted me to goe, provided that I should returne quickly. After this resolution he sent for me, and likewise the Queene Mother, and commanded me to goe finde the sayd Lord *Mansfield* in the place, where I was to serve him in all I could, for the cure of his hurt; I went and found him, having with me a letter from their Majesties: having seene it, he received me with a good will, and from thenceforth discharged three other Chirurgions that drest him; which was to my great greefe, because his hurt seemed to me uncureable. Now at *Bourgueil* there were retired divers gentlemen, who had beene hurt at the sayd battell, knowing that Mounsieur *de Guise* was there, who had been also very much hurt with a Pistoll shot through one legge, well assured that he would have good Chirurgions to dresse him, and also that hee being kind and liberall, would assist them with a great part of their necessities. And for my part, I did helpe and ayd them in my Art as much as it was possible; some dyed, some recovered, according to their hurts. The Count *Ringrave* died, who had such a shot in the shoulder, as the King of *Navarre* before *Rouen*. Monsieure *de Bassompiere* Colonell of twelve hundred horse, was hurt also in such a like place as Count *Mansfield*, whom I drest and God cured. God so well blessed my worke that within three weekes I led him back to *Paris*, where I must yet make some incisions in the arme of the sayd Lord *Mansfield*, to draw out the bones which were greatly broken and caries'd: he was cured by the grace of God, and gave me an honest reward, so that I was well contented with him and he with me, as he hath since made it appeare: he writ a letter to the Duke of *Ascot* how that he was cured of his hurt, and also Monsieur *de Bassompiere* of his, and divers others, which I had dress't after the battell of *Moncontour*, and counselled him to beseech the King of *France* my good master, to give me leave to goe see Monsieur the Marquesse of *Auret* his brother.

Voyage of Flanders.

Monsieur the Duke of *Ascot* did not faile to send a Gentleman to the King with a letter, humbly to beseech him to doe him so much good and honour, as to permit and command his cheefe Chirurgion to come see the Marquesse of *Auret* his brother; who had received a Musket shot neare the knee, with fracture of the bone, about seaven monthes since, with the Physitions and Chirurgions in those parts were much troubled to cure. The King sent for me, and commanded me to goe see the said Lord *Auret*, and to helpe him in all that I could for the cure of his hurt; I told him I would imploy all that little knowledge which it had pleased God to give me. I went then conducted by two Gentlemen to the Castle of *Auret*, which is a league and a halfe from *Mounts* in *Hainault*, where the said Marquesse was: as soone as I arrived I visited him, and told him the King had commanded me to come see him, and to dresse him of his hurt; he told me he was glad of my comming, and was much bound to the King to have done him the honour, to have sent me to him. I found him in a great Feaver, his eyes very much sunke, with a countenance gastly and yellow, his tongue drie and rough, and all the

body emaciated and leane, his speech low like that of a
dying man: then I found his thigh much swelled, apostemated, ulcerated, and casting out a greene stinking matter;
I searcht it with a silver probe, and by the same I found a
cavity neare the groyne, ending in the middle of the thigh,
and others about the knee, sanious and cuniculous;[1] also
certaine scales of bones some separated, others not. The
Legge was much tumified, and soaked with a pituitous
humor, cold, moist, and flatulent; in so much that the
naturall heate was in the way to be suffocated, and extinguished, and the said Legge crooked and retracted
toward the buttockes, his rumpe ulcerated the breadth of
the palme of an hand, and he said he felt there a great paine
and smarting, and likewise in his reines, in so much that hee
could not take any rest night or day; neither had hee any
appetite to eate, but to drinke enough; it was told mee hee
fell often into faintings and swoonings, and sometimes
as it were into an Epilepsie, and had oftentimes desire to
vomit, with such a trembling that hee could not carry his
hands to his mouth. Seeing and considering all these great
accidents, and the forces much abated; truly I was much
grieved to have gone to him, because me thought there
was little appearance that he could escape. Notwithstanding
to give him courage and good hope, I told him, that I
would quickly set him on foote by the grace of God, and
the Physitions and Chirurgions helpe. Having seene him,
I went a walking into a Garden, where I prayed to God
that hee would give me the grace to cure him, and that hee
would give a blessing to our hands, and medicaments, to
combate against so many complicated maladies. I bethought
in my minde the wayes I must keepe to doe it. They called
mee to dinner, I entred into the kitchin where I saw taken
out of a great pot, halfe a Mutton, a quarter of Veale, three
great peeces of Beefe, and two Pullets, and a great peece
of Bacon, with great store of good Hearbes. Then I
said to my selfe this broth was full of juice, and of good

---

[1] i.e. full of holes and windings.

nourishment; After dinner all the Physitions and Chirurgions assembled, we entred into conference in the presence of Monsieur the Duke of *Ascot*, and some Gentlemen that did accompany him; I began to tell the Chirurgions that I mervailed much they had made no apertions in the Marquesses thigh, which was all apostemated, and the matter which issued out was very foule and stinking, which shewed it had a long time lurked there, and that I had found with my probe a *Caries* in the bone, and small scales which were already separated; they made mee answer, hee would never give consent, and likewise it was almost two monthes since they could winne him to put on cleane sheets on his bed, neither durst one scarce touch the coverlet, he feelt so great paine. Then said I, for to cure him, we must touch other things than the coverlet of the bed. Each one said what hee thought best of the Lords greefe, and for conclusion held it altogether deplorable. I told them there was yet some hope, because of his youth, and that God and nature doe sometime such things which seeme to Physitions and Chirurgions to bee impossible. My consultation was, that all these accidents were come by reason of the bullet hitting neare the joynt of the knee, which had broken the Ligaments, tendons, and *aponeuroses* of the muscles which tye the sayd joynt together with the *Os femoris*; also nerves, veines, and arteries from whence had followed paine, inflammation, aposteme and ulcer: and that wee must begin the cure by the disease, which was the cause of all the sayd accidents, that is to say, to make apertions to give issue to the matter reteined in the interspaces of the muscles, and in the substance of them: Likewise to the bones which caused a great corruption in the whole thigh, from whence the vapors did arise and were carryed to the heart, which caused the sincope, and the feaver; and the feaver an universall heate through the whole body; and by consequent, depravation of the whole *Oeconomie*; Likewise that the said vapours were communicated to the braine, which caused the Epilipsie, and trembling, and to the stomacke

disdaine and loathing, and hindred it from doing his functions, which are cheefely to concoct and disgest the meate,
and to convert it into *Chylus*; which not being well con-
cocted, they ingender crudities and obstructions, which
makes that the parts are not nourished, and by consequent the body dryes, and growes leane; and because also
it did not doe any exercise, for every part which hath not
his motion remaineth languid, and *atrophiated*, because the
heate & spirits are not sent or drawne thither, from whence
followes mortification. And to nourish and fatten the body,
frictions must be made universally through the whole body,
with warme linnen cloathes, above, below, on the right
side, and left, and round about: to the end to draw the
blood and spirits from within outward, and to resolve any
fuliginous vapours retained betweene the skinne, and the
flesh; thereby the parts shall be nourished and restored, (as
I have heretofore sayd in the tenth booke treating of wounds
of Gunshot) and wee must then cease when we see heate
and rednesse in the skinne, for feare of resolving that wee
have already drawne, and by consequent make it become
more leane. As for the Ulcer which he had upon his rumpe,
which came through too long lying upon it without being
remooved, which was the cause that the spirits could not
florish or shine in it; by the meanes of which there should
bee inflammation, aposteme and then ulcer, yea with losse
of substance of the subject flesh, with a very great paine;
because of the nerves which are disseminated in this part.
That wee must likewise put him into another soft bed, and
give him a cleane shirt, and sheets; otherwise all that wee
could doe would serve for nothing, because that those excrements and vapors of the matter retained so long in his
bed, are drawne in by the Systole and Diastole of the
Arteries which are disseminated through the skin, and
cause the spirits to change and acquire an ill quality and
corruption; which is seene in some that shall lye in a bed
where one hath sweate for the Pox, who will get the Pox
by the putrid vapours which shall remaine soaked in the

sheets and coverlets. Now the cause why he could in no
wise sleepe, and was as it were in a consumption, t'was
because he eate little, and did not doe any exercise, and
because hee was grieved with extreame paine. For there is
nothing that abateth so much the strength as paine. The
cause why his tongue was dry and fowle, was through the
vehemence of the heate of the feaver, by the vapors which
ascended through the whole body to the mouth. For as we
say in a common proverb, when an Oven is well heate, the
throate feeles it. Having discoursed of the causes and accidents, I sayd they must be cured by their contraries, and
first we must appease the paine, making apertions in the
thigh to evacuate the matter retained, not evacuating all
at a time for feare least by a sodaine great evacuation there
might happen a great decay of spirits, which might much
weaken the patient and shorten his dayes. Secondly, to
looke unto the great swelling and cold in his Legge, fearing
least it should fall into a Gangreene; and that actuall heate
must bee applyed unto him because the potentiall could
not reduce the intemperature *de rotentia ad actum*; for this
cause hot brickes must bee applyed round about, on which
should bee cast a decoction of nervall hearbes boyled in
wine and Vinegar, then wrapt up in some napkin, and to
the feete an earthen bottle filled with the sayd decoction,
stopt and wrapt up with some linnen clothes; also that
fomentations must be made upon the thigh, and the whole
Legge, of a decoction made of Sage, Rosemary, Time,
Lavender, flowers of Camomile, melilot, and red Roses
boyled in white wine, and a *Lixivium* made with oake ashes
with a little Vinegar, and halfe an handfull of salt. This
decoction hath vertue to attenuate, incise, resolve and drye
the grosse viscous humor. The sayd fomentations must bee
used a long while, to the end there may bee a greater
resolution; for being so done a long time together, more is
resolved than attracted, because the humor contained in the
part is liquified, the skin and the flesh of the muscles is
rarified. Thirdly, that there must be applyed upon the

rumpe a great emplaster made of the red desiccative and *Unguentum Comitissæ* of each equall parts incorporated together, to the end to appease his paine and dry up the Ulcer, also to make him a little downe pillow which might beare his rumpe aloft without leaning upon it. Fourthly to refresh the heate of his kidneys one should apply the unguent called *Refrigerans Galeni* freshly made, and upon that the leaves of water Lillies. Then a napkin dipt in *Oxycrate*, wrung out and often renewed: and for the corroboration and strengthening of his heart a refreshing medicine should bee applyed made with oyle of *nenuphar*, and unguent of Roses and a little saffron dissolved in Rose Vinegar, and Treakle spread upon a peece of Scarlet cloth. For the *Sincope* which proceded from the debilitation of the naturall strength troubling the braine also, he must use good nourishment full of juice, as rere[1] egges, Damaske prunes stewed in wine and sugar, also *Panada* made with the broth of the great pot (of which I have already spoken) with the white fleshy parts of Capons, and Partridge wings minced small, and other rostmeate easie of disgestion, as Veale, Goate, Pigeon, Partridge, and the like. The sauce should be Orenges, Verjuice, Sorrell, sharpe Pomegranets; and that he should likewise eate of them boyled with good hearbes; as Sorrell, Lettice, Purslan, Succory, Buglosse, Marygolds, and other the like. At night hee might use cleansed barley with juice of *Nenuphar* and Sorrell, of each two ounces, with five or six graines of *Opium* and of the foure cold seedes bruised, of each halfe an ounce, which is a remedy nourishing and medicinall, which will provoke him to sleepe: that his bread should be of Maslin,[2] neither too new nor too stale; and for the great paine of his head, his haire must be cut, and rub his head with *Oxirrhodinum* luke warme, and leave a double cloth wet therein upon it; likewise should be made for him a frontall of oyle of Roses, *Nenuphar*, Poppies, and a little *opium* and Rose Vinegar, and a little Campher and to renew it sometimes. Moreover

---

[1] i.e. rear, or soft-boiled.   [2] i.e. bread made of mixed grains.

one should cause him to smell to the flowers of Henbane and *Nenuphar* bruised with Viniger Rosewater, and a little campher wrapped in a handkercher, which shall be often and a long time held to his nose to the end that the smell may be communicated to the braine, and these things to be continued till that the great inflammation and paine be past, for feare of cooling the braine too much. Besides, one may cause it to raine artificially in powring downe from some high place into a kettle, and that it make such a noyse that the patient may heare it, by these meanes sleepe shall bee provoked on him. And as for the retraction of his Legge that there was hope to redresse it, when evacuation was made of the matter and other humors contained in the thigh, which by their extention (made by repletion) have drawne backe the Leg, which might be remedied in rubbing the whole joynt of the knee with *Unguentum Dialthæa* and oyle of Lillies, and a little *aqua vitæ*, and upon it to be laid, blacke wooll with the grease thereof. Likewise putting in the hamme a feather-pillow foulded in double, and by little and little to make his Leg to stretch out. All which my discourse was well approoved of by the Physitions and Chirurgions: the consultation ended wee went to the sicke patient, and I made him three apertions in his thigh, from whence issued out great quantity of matter and *Sanies*; and at the same time I drew out some scales of bones, nor would I let out too much aboundance of the said matter for feare of too much decaying his strength: Then two or three houres after I caused a bed to bee made neare his owne, where there were cleane white sheets; then a strong man lifted him into it, and rejoyced much in that hee was taken out of his foule stinking bed. Soone after hee demanded to sleepe, which hee did almost foure houres, where all the people of the house began to rejoyce, cheefely Monsieur the Duke of *Ascot* his brother.

The dayes following I made injections into the bottome and cavities of the Ulcer, made with *Ægyptiacum*, dissolved sometimes in *aqua vitæ*, and sometimes in wine. I applyed to mundifie and dry the spongie and loose flesh, bolsters, at the bottome of the sinuosityes hollow tents of Lead, that the *Sanies* might have passage out; and upon it a greate Emplaster of *Diacalcitheos* dissolved in wine: likewise I did rowle it with such dexterity, that he had no paine, which being appeased the fever began much to diminish. Then I made him drinke wine moderately allayed with water, knowing that it restores and quickens the spirits: and all the things which we rested on in the consultation were accomplisht, according to time, and order; and his paines and fever ceased, he began to grow better, and discharged two of his Chirurgions, and one of his Physitions, so that we were but three with him. Now I remained thereabout two monethes, which was not without seeing divers sicke people, as well rich as poore which came to me three or foure leagues about. They gave meate and drinke to the needy, all which he recommended to me, and prayed me also for his sake to helpe them. I protest I did not refuse any one, and did to them what I possibly could, whereof he was joyfull. Then when I saw he began to mend, I told him hee must have a consort of Violons & a jester to make him merry, which he did: in one moneth we so wrought, that he could hold himselfe up in a chaire, and made himselfe to be carried and walke in his garden, and at the gate of his Castle to see the people passe by. The Countrey people of two or three leagues about, knowing they could see him, came the feast day male and female, to sing and dance pell mell, in joy of his amendment, all being very glad to see him, which was not done without good laughing and drinking. He caus'd still a barrell of beere to be given them, and they dranke all merrily to his good health. And the Citizens of *Mont Hainault* and other gentlemen neighbours came to see him in admiration, as a man coming from the tombe. And as soone as he began to mend, he was not without company, and as one went out another came in, to visite him: his table was alwayes well covered. Hee was greatly loved of the Nobility, and of the common people,

as well for his liberality as by reason of his beauty, and
honesty, having a pleasant looke and a gracious speech,
insomuch that those that beheld his face were constrained
to love him. The cheefe of the City of *Monts* came on
Saturday to beseech him to permit mee to goe to *Monts*,
where they had a great desire to feast, and make me good
cheere for his sake. He told them he would pray me to goe
there, which he did. But I made them answere that they
should not doe me so much honour, as also that they could
not give me better cheere than I had with him. And he
prayed mee againe affectionately to goe thither, and that I
should doe that for his sake, to which I agreed. The day
after they fetcht me with two Coaches, and being arrived
at *Monts* we found the dinner ready, and the cheefe of the
Citty with their wives, stayed for mee with a good will.
We went to the Table and they placed me at the upper end,
and dranke all to me, and to the health of Monsieur *D'auret*,
saying that he was very happy, and they likewise to have
obtained me to take him in hand, for that they knew that
in this company, he was greatly honoured and loved. After
dinner they led mee backe to the Castle of *Auret*, where
Monsieur the Marquesse stayd for me with great expectation to recount unto him, what we had done in our banquet, I told him that all the company had dranke divers
times to his health: in 6 weekes he began to uphold himselfe a little with crutches, and to grow very fat and get a
lively naturall colour. Now he had a desire to goe to
Beaumont which is the dwelling place of Monsieur the Duke
of *Ascot*, and made himselfe be carried in a great chaire with
eight men by turnes, and the Country folkes where we
passed along, knowing 'twas Monsieur the Marquesse
fought and strove together who should carry him, and
constrained us to drinke, but it was but Beere, but I
beleeve had it beene Wine or Hippocras they would have
given it us with a very good will, so much did they shew
themselves joyfull to see the sayd Marquesse, and prayd all
to God for him. Being arrived at *Beaumont* all the people

came before us to doe him reverence, and prayed God to blesse him, and keepe him in good health. We entred into the Castle where there was more than 50 gentlemen which the Duke of *Ascot* had sent for to come make good cheere with his brother, who kept his table furnisht three dayes together. After dinner the gentlemen runne at the Ring, playd at Foyles, and rejoyced greatly to see Monsieur *Auret*, because they had heard he would never come out of his bed againe, or be cured of his hurt. I was alwayes at the upper end of the table, where every one dranke carouses to him, & me, thinking to make me foxt, which they could not do: for I drank but according to my old custome. A few dayes after wee returned backe and tooke leave of Madam the Dutchesse of *Ascot,* who tooke a Diamond ring from her finger which she gave me, acknowledging I had very well drest her brother; which Diamond was more worth than fifty Crownes. Monsieur *Auret* grew still better and better, and walked all alone round about his garden with crutches. I beg'd leave of him divers times, to come away to *Paris*, declaring that his Physition, and Chirurgion, would well doe the rest that remained, for the cure of his greefe. And now to begin a little to estrange my selfe from him, I prayd him to give me leave to goe see the Citty of *Antwerp*, which he willingly accorded to: and commanded his Steward to conduct me thither accompanied with two Pages: we passed through *Malignes* and *Bruxelle*, where the cheefe of the Citty prayed the sayd Steward, that at our returne they might heare of it; and that they had a great desire to feast me, as they of *Monts* had done. I thank't them most kindly, and told them that I was not worthy of such honour; I was two dayes and a halfe to see the Citty of *Antwerp*, where some Merchants knowing the Steward, prayd him to doe them the honour, that they might bestow a dinner or supper upon us. There was striving who should have us, and were all very joyfull to heare of the good health of the Marquesse of *Auret*, doing me more honour than I expected. To conclude, we came backe to the Marquesse making good cheere, and within five or sixe dayes I asked my leave of him, which he granted with great greefe, and gave me an honest Present, and of great valew, and made me be conducted by the sayd master of his house and two Pages, even to my house at *Paris*.

I have forgot to tell you, that the *Spaniards* have since ruined, and demolisht his Castle of *Auret*, sack't, pillage'd, rifled and burnt all the houses, and Villages belonging unto him, because he would not be of their side, in the slaughters and ruines of the Low Countryes.

The Voyage of Bourges, 1562.

The King with his Campe remained not long at *Bourges*, but those within yeelded it up, and went out with their jewells saved. I know nothing worthy of memory, but that a Boy of the Kings privie kitchin, who being neere the walls of the Citty before the composition was made, cryed with a loud voyce, Huguenot, huguenot, shoot heere, shoote heere, having his armes lifted up, and his hand stretched out; a souldier shot his hand quite through with a bullet: having received his stroake, he came and found me out to dresse him. My Lord high Constable, seeing the Boy to have his hand all bloody, and all rent and torne; demanded of him who had hurt him. Then there was a gentleman who saw the shot made, sayd it was well bestow'd because he cried, *Huguenot*, shoot here, shoot here. Then the sayd Lord Constable sayd this *Huguenot* was a good musketiere, and bare a pittifull mind, for it was very likely if he would have shot at his head, he might have done it more easily than in the hand. I dress'd the sayd Cooke who was very sicke, but at length was cured, but with lamenesse of his hand, and ever since his companions call him *Huguenot*; he is living.

The battell of Saint Denis, 1567.

And as for the battell of Saint *Denis*, there were divers slaine aswell on one side as on the other: ours being hurt, went backe to *Paris* to be dressed together with the Prisoners who were taken, whereof I dressed a great part. The King commanded me by the request of the Lady high Constable, to goe to her house to dresse my Lord, who had received a Pistoll shot in the middle of the spondills of his backe, whereby he presently lost all sence and motion of thighes and legges, with retention of excrements, not being able to cast out his Urine, nor anything by the fundament, because that the spinall marrow, (from whence proceede the sinewes to give sense and motion to the inferiour parts,) was bruised, broken, and torne by the vehemence of the bullet. He likewise lost his reason, and understanding, and in a few dayes he dyed. The Chirurgions of *Paris* were a long time troubled to dresse the sayd wounded people, I beleeve (my little master) that you saw some of them. I beseech the great God of Victories, that we may never be imployed in such evill encounters, and disasters.

The voyage of Bayonne, 1564.

Now I say moreover, what I did in the voyage with the King to *Bayonne*, where we have beene two yeares and more to compasse all this Kingdome, where in divers Citties and Villages I have beene called into consultations for divers diseases, with the deceased Monsieur *Chaplaine* cheefe Phisition to the King, and Monsieur *Chastellan* cheefe to the Queene Mother, a man of great honour and knowledge in Physicke and Chirurgery: making this voyage I was alwayes inquisitive of the Chirurgions if they had marked any rare thing of remarke in their practice, to the end to learne some new thing. Being at *Bayonne* there happened two things of remarke for the young Chirurgions. The first was, that I drest a *Spanish* Gentleman, who had a greevous great impostume in his throate: he came to have beene touched by the deceased King *Charles* for the Evill. I made incision in his Aposteme, where there was found great quantity of creeping wormes as bigge as the point of a spindle, having a blacke head; and there was great quantity of rotten flesh. Moreover there was under his tongue an impostume called *Ranula*, which hindred him to utter forth his words, and to eate and swallow his meate: he pray'd mee with his held up hands to open it for him if it could be done without perill of his person, which I immediatly did, and found under my Lancet a solid body, which was five stones like those which are drawne from the bladder. The greatest was as big as an Almond and the other like little long Beanes, which were five in number; in this aposteme was contained a slimy humor of a yellow colour which was more than foure spoonefulls; I left him in the hands of a Chirurgion of the Citty to finish the cure.

Monsieur *de Fontaine* Knight of the Kings Order, had a great continuall pestilent Feaver, accompanyed with divers Carboncles in divers parts of his body, who was two dayes without ceasing to bleed at nose, nor could it be stancht; and by that meanes the feaver ceased with a very great sweat, and soone after the Charboncles ripened and were by me dressed and by the grace of God cured.

I have publisht this Apologie to the end that each man may know, with what foot I have always marched, and I thinke there is not any man so ticklish, which taketh not in good part what I have said, seeing my discourse is true, and that the effect sheweth the thing to the eye, reason being my warrant against all Calumnies.

The end of the Apologie and Voyages.

PART TWO

ANNO
ÆTATIS. 72
1582

AMBROISE PARÉ

ÆT. 72

Engraved by Stephanus Delaulne 1582

SELECTIONS FROM THE SURGICAL WRITINGS OF AMBROISE PARÉ

INTRODUCTION

What Chyrurgerie is.

CHYRURGERIE is an Art, which teacheth the way by reason, how by the operation of the hand we may cure prevent and mitigate diseases, which accidentally happen unto us. Others have thought good to describe it otherwise, as that; it is that part of Physicke which undertaketh the cure of diseases by the sole industry of the hand; as by cutting, burning, sawing off, uniting fractures, restoring dislocations, and performing other workes, of which we shall hereafter treate. Chyrurgery also is thus defined by the Author of the medicinall Definitions; The quicke motion of an intrepide hand joyned with experience: or an artificiall action by the hands used in Physicke, for some convenient intent. Yet none must thinke to attaine to any great perfection in this Art, without the helpe of the other two parts of Physicke; I say of Diet and Pharmacie, and the divers application of proper medicines, respecting the condition of the causes, diseases, symptomes, and the like circumstances, which comprehended under the names of things naturall, not naturall, and besides nature (as they commonly call them) wee intend to describe in their proper place. But if any reply, that there be many which doe the workes of Chirurgery, without any

(marginal notes:) The definition of Chirurgerie.

What necessary for a Chirurgion.

knowledge of such like things, who notwithstanding have cured desperate diseases with happy successe; let them take this for an answer, that such things happen rather by chance, than by the industry of the Art, and that they are not provident that commit themselves to such. Because that for some one happy chance, a thousand dangerous errors happen afterwards, as *Galen* (in divers places of his Method) speakes against the Emperickes. Wherefore seeing wee have set downe Chirurgery to be a diligent operation of the hands, strengthened by the assistance of Diet and Pharmacie, wee will now shew, what, and of what nature the operations of it are.

Of Chirurgicall operations.

The nature of a Chirurgion.

Five things are proper to the dutie of a Chirurgian; To take away that which is superfluous; to restore to their places, such things as are displaced; to separate those things which are joyned together; to joyne those which are separated; and to supply the defects of nature. Thou shalt fare more easily and happily attaine to the knowledge of these things by long use and much exercise, than by much reading of Bookes, or daily hearing of Teachers. For speech how perspicuous and elegant soever it be, cannot so vively expresse any thing, as that which is subjected to the faithfull eyes and hands.

Experience more necessary for a Chirurgion, than Art.

Examples of taking away that which is superfluous.

Wee have examples of taking away that which abounds, in the amputation, or cutting off a finger, if any have sixe on one hand, or any other monstrous member that may grow out: in the lopping off a putrified part inwardly corrupted; in the extraction of a dead child, the secondine, mole or such like bodies out of a womans wombe; in taking downe of all Tumors, as Wens, Warts, Polypus, Cancers, and fleshy excrescenses of the like nature; in the pulling forth of bullets, of peeces of maile, of darts, arrowes, shells, splinters, and of all kind of weapons in what part of the body soever they be. And hee taketh away that which redounds, which plucks away the haires of the eye-lids which trouble the eye by their turning in towards it: who cuts away the web, possessing all the *Adnata, and part of the *Cornea: who letteth forth suppurated matter; who taketh out stones in what part soever of the body they grow; who puls out a rotten or otherwise hurtfull tooth, or cuts a naile that runs into the flesh; who cuts away part of the *uvula*, or haires that grow on the eye-lids; who taketh off a Cataract; who cuts the navill or fore-skinne of a child newly borne, or the skinnie caruncles of womens privities.

* Two tunicles of the eyes.

Examples of placing those things which are out of their naturall site, are manifest in restoring dislocated bones; in replacing of the guts and kall fallen into the cods, or out of the navill or belly by a wound, or of the falling downe of the wombe, fundament, or great gut, or the eye hanging out of its circle, or proper place.

Examples of replacing.

But wee may take examples of disjoyning those things which are continued from the fingers growing together, either by some chance, as burning, or by the imbecilitie of the forming facultie: by the disjunction of the membrane called *Hymen*, or any other troubling the necke of the wombe, by the dissection of the ligament of the tongue, which hinders children from sucking and speaking, and of that which hinders the *Glans* from being uncovered of the foreskinne; by the devision of a varicous veine, or of a halfe cut nerve or tendon, causing convulsion: by the division of the membrane stopping the auditory passage, the nose, mouth, or fundament, or the stubborne sticking together of the haires of the eye-lids. Referre to this place all the workes done by Causticks, the Saw, Trepan, Lancet, Cuppingglasses, Incision Knife, Leaches, either for evacuation, derivation or revulsion sake.

Example of separating things joyned together.

The Chirurgion drawes together things separated, which healeth wounds by stitching them, by bolstering, binding, giving rest to, and fit placing the part: which repaires fractures; restores luxated parts; who by binding the vessell, staieth the violent effusion of bloud: who cicatriseth cloven

Examples of uniting things disjoyned.

lips, commonly called hare-lips; who reduces to equalitie the cavities of Ulcers, and Fistula's.

Examples of suplying defects.

But hee repaires those things which are defective, either from the infancy, or afterwards by accident, as much as Art and Nature will suffer, who sets on an eare, an eye, a nose, one or more teeth; who fils the hollownesse of the palat eaten by the Poxe, with a thinne plate of gold or silver, or such like; who supplies the defect of the tongue in part cut off, by some new addition; who fastens to a hand, an arme or legge with fit ligaments workemanlike: who fits a doublet bumbasted, or made with iron plates to make the body straight; who fills a shooe too big with corke, or fastens a stocking or socke to a lame mans girdle to helpe his gate. We will treate more fully of all these in our following Worke. But in performing those things with the hands, we cannot but cause paine: (for who can without paine cut off an arme, or legge, devide and teare asunder the necke of the bladder, restore bones put out of their places, open ulcers, bind up wounds, and apply cauteries, and doe such like?) notwithstanding the matter often comes to that passe, that unlesse wee use a judicious hand, wee must either die, or leade the remnant of our lives in perpetuall misery. Who therefore can justly abhorre a Chirurgion for this, or accuse him of crueltie? or desire they may be served, as in ancient times the Romanes served *Archagalus*, who at the first made him free of the Citie, but presently after, because he did somwhat too cruelly burne, cut and performe the other workes of a good Chirurgion, they drew him from his house into the Campus Martius and there stoned him to death, as wee have read it recorded by *Sextus Cheroneus Plutarche's* Neece by his daughter. Truly it was an inhumane kind of ingratitude, so cruelly to murder a man intent to the workes of so necessary an Art. But the Senate could not approve the act, wherefore to expiate the crime as well as then they could, they made his Statue in gold, placed it in *Æsculapius* his Temple, and dedicated it to his perpetuall memorie. For my part I very well like

Archagalus the Chirurgion.

that saying of *Celsus*; A Chirurgeon must have a strong, *In praefat.*
stable, and intrepide hand, and a minde resolute and merci- *lib.* 7.
lesse; so that to heale him he taketh in hand, he be not
moved to make more haste than the thing requires; or to
cut lesse than is needfull; but which doth all things as if he The proper-
were nothing affected with their cries; not giving heed to ties of a good
the judgement of the vaine common people, who Chirurgion.
speake ill of Chirurgions because
of their ignorance.

OF ANEURISMAS

Of an Aneurisma, *that is, the dilatation, or springing of an*
Artery, veine, or Sinnew.

AN *Aneurisma* is a soft tumor yeelding to the touch, made
by the bloud and spirit powred forth under the flesh What it is.
and Muscles, by the dilatation or relaxation of an Artery.
Yet the author of the definitions seemes to call any dilatation of any venous vessell by the name of an *Aneurisma*.
Galen calls an *Aneurisma* an opening made of the *Anasto-*
mosis of an Artery. Also an *Aneurisma* is made, when an
Artery that is wounded closeth too slowly, the substance
which is above it being in the meane time agglutinated,
filled with flesh and cicatrized, which doth not seldome
happen in opening of Arteries unskilfully performed and
negligently cured; therefore *Aneurismaes* are absolutely In what
made by the *Anastomosis*, springing, breaking, *Erosion*, and parts they
wounding of the Arteries. These happen in all parts of chiefly hap-
the body, but more frequently in the throat, especially in pen.
women after a painfull travaile. For when as they more
strongly strive to hold their breath, for the more powerfull
expulsion of the birth, it happens that the Artery is dilated
and broken, whence followes an effusion of bloud and
spirits under the skin. The signes are, a swelling, one while

great, another small, with a pulsation and a colour not varying from the native constitution of the skinne. It is a soft tumor, and so yeelding to the impression of the fingers that if it peradventure be small, it wholy vanisheth, the Arterious bloud and spirits flying backe into the body of the Artery, but presently assoone as you take your fingers away, they returne againe with like celerity. Some *Aneurismaes* doe not onely when they are pressed, but also of themselves make a sensible hissing, if you lay your eare neare to them, by reason of the motion of the vitall spirit rushing with great violence through the straitnes of the passage.

Prognosticks.   Wherefore in *Aneurismaes* in which there is a great rupture of the Artery, such a noyse is not heard, because the spirit is carryed through a larger passage. Great *Aneurismaes* under the Arme pits, in the Groines and in other parts wherein there are large vessells, admit no cure, because so great an eruption of blood and spirit often followes uppon such an incision, that death prevents both art and Cure.

A History.   Which I observed a few yeares agoe in a certaine preist of Saint *Andrewes* of the Arches, M. *John Maillet* dwelling with the chiefe President *Christopher de Thou*. Who having

Aneurismaes must not rashly be opened.   an *Aneurisma* at the setting on of the shoulder about the bignes of a Wall-nut, I charged him, hee should not let it be opened, for if he did, it would bring him into manifest danger of his life, and that it would be more safe for him, to breake the violence thereof with double clothes steeped in the juyce of Night-shade and Houseleeke, with new and whayey cheese mixt therewith: Or with *Unguentum de Bolo* or *Emplastrum contra rupturam* and such other refrigerating and astringent medicines, if hee would lay upon it a thin plate of Lead, and would use shorter breeches that his doublet might serve to hold it too, to which hee might fasten his breeches instead of a swathe, and in the meane time he should eschew all things which attenuate and inflame the blood, but especially he should keepe himselfe from all great straining of his voyce. Although he had used this Diet for a yeare, yet he could not so handle the matter but that the tumor increased, which he observing goes to a Barber, who supposing the tumor to be of the kinde of vulgar inpostumes, applies to it in the Evening a Causticke causing an Eschar so to open it. In the Morning such an abundance of blood flowed forth from the tumor being opened, that he therewith astonished, implores all possible ayde, and bidds that I should be called to stay this his great bleeding, and he repented that he had not followed my directions. Wherefore I am called, but when I was scarce over the threshould, he gave up his ghost with his blood. Wherefore I diligently admonish the young Chirurgion that hee do not rashly open *Aneurismas* unlesse they be small in an ignoble part, and not indued with large vessells, but rather let him performe the cure after this manner. Cut the skinne which lyes over it untill the Artery appeare, and then separate it with your knife from the particles about it, then thrust a blunt and crooked needle with a thred in it under it, binde it, then cut it off and so expect the falling off, of the thred of it selfe whiles nature covers the orifices of the cut Artery with new flesh, then the residue of the cure may be performed after the manner of simple wounds. The *Aneurismaes* which happen in the internall parts are uncurable. Such as frequently happen to those who have often had the unction and sweat for the cure of the French disease, because the blood, being so attenuated and heated therewith that it cannot be contayned in the receptacles of the Artery, it distends it to that largenesse as to hold a mans fist; Which I have observed in the dead body of a certaine Taylor, who by an *Aneurisma* of the Arterious veine suddenly whilest hee was playing at Tennis fell downe dead, the vessell being broken: his body being opened I found a great quantity of blood powred forth into the Capacity of the Chest, but the body of the Artery was dilated to that largenesse I formerly mentioned, and the inner Coate thereof was bony. For which cause within a while after I shewed it to the great admiration of the beholders in the

How they must be cured.

These of the inward parts incureable.

A History.

Physitions Schole whilest I publiquely dissected a body there; the whilst he lived said he felt a beating and a great heate over all his body by the force of the pulsation of all the Arteryes, by occasion whereof hee often swounded. Doctor *Sylvius* the Kings professor of Physicke at that time forbad him the use of Wine, and wished him to use boyled water for his drinke, and Crudds and new Cheeses for his meate, and to apply them in forme of Cataplasmes upon the grieved and swolne part. At night he used a ptisan of Barley meale and Poppy-seedes, and was purged now and then with a Clyster of refrigerating and emollient things, or with Cassia alone, by which medicines hee said hee found himselfe much better. The cause of such a bony constitution of the Arteries by *Aneurismaes* is, for that the hot and fervid blood first dilates the Coates of an Artery, then breakes them; which when it happens, it then borrowes from the neighbouring bodies a fit matter to restore the loosed continuity thereof.

This matter whilest by little and little it is dried and hardened, it degenerates into a Gristely or else a bony substance, just by the force of the same materiall and efficient causes, by which stones are generated in the reines and bladder. For the more terrestriall portion of the blood is dried and condensed by the power of the unnaturall heat contayned in the part affected with an *Aneurismae*; whereby it comes to passe that the substance added to the dilated and broken Artery is turned into a body of a bony consistence. In which the singular providence of nature, the handmaide of God is shewed, as that which, as it were by making and opposing a new wall or bancke, would hinder and breake the violence of the raging blood swelling with the abundance of the vitall spirits; unlesse any had rather to refer the cause of that hardnesse to the continuall application of refrigerating and astringent medicines. Which have power to condensate and harden, as may not obscurely be gathered by the writings of *Galen*. But beware you be not deceived by the forementioned signes; For sometimes in

Lib. 4. *Cap. ult. de praef. ex pulsu.*

large *Aneurismaes* you can perceive no pulsation, neither can you force the blood into the Artery by the pressure of your fingers, either because the quantity of such blood is greater than which can be contayned in the ancient receptacles of the Artery, or because it is condensate and concrete into Clods, whereupon wanting the benefit of ventilation from the heart, it presently putrifies; Thence ensue great paine, a Gangren, and mortification of the part, and lastly the death of the Creature.

A Caution in the knowing of Aneurismaes.

OF HERNIA

Of the Tumors of the Groines and Codds, called Herniæ, *that is, Ruptures.*

THE ancient Phisitions have made many kindes of Ruptures, yet indeede there are onely three to be called by that name, that is, the *Intestinalis*, or that of the guts, the *Zirbalis*, or that of the kall, and that which is mixed of them both. The other kindes of Ruptures have come into this order, rather by similitude, than any truth of the thing: for in them the Gut, or Kall doe not forsake their places.

There are onely 3. sorts of Ruptures.

The Greekes have given to all these severall names, both from the seat of the tumor, as also from their matter. For thus they have called an unperfect rupture which descends not beyond the Groines, nor falls downe into the Codds, *Bubonocele*: but the compleate which penetrates into the Codde, if it be by falling downe of the Gut, *Enterocele*: if from the Kall, *Epiplocele*; if from them both together, they name it *Entero-epiplocele*: but if the tumor proceede from a waterish humor, they terme it *Hydrocele*; if from winde, *Physocele*, if from both, *Hydrophysocele*; if a fleshie excrescence shall grow about the testicle, or in the substance thereof, it is named *Sarcocele*. If the veines interwoven, and

Bubonocele.
Enterocele and Epiplocele.
Hydrocele.
Physocele.
Sarcocele.

Cirsocele.

divaricated diverse wayes shall be swollen in the Codde and Testicles, the tumor obtaines the name of a *Cirsocele*. But if the humors shall be shut up, or sent thither, the name is imposed upon the tumor, from the predominant humor, as we have noted in the beginning of our Tractate of tumors. The causes are many, as all too violent motions, a stroake, a fall from a high place, vomiting, a cough, leaping, riding upon a trotting horse, the sounding of trumpets, or sackbuts, the carrying, or lifting up of a heavy burden, racking, also the too immoderate use of viscide and flatulent meates; for all such things may either relaxe or breake the *Peritonæum*, as that which is a thinne and extended membrane. The signes of a *Bubonocele* are a round tumor in the Groine, which pressed, is easily forced in. The signes of an *Enterocele*, are a hard tumor in the Codde, which forced, returneth backe and departeth with a certaine murmour and paine; but the tumor proceeding of the Kall, is laxe and feeles soft like Wooll, and which is more difficultly forced in, than that which proceeds from the Guts, but yet without murmuring and paine: for the substance of the Guts, seeing it is one, and continued to it selfe, they doe not onely mutually succeede each other, but by a certaine consequence doe, as in a dance draw each other, so to avoide distention, which in their membranous body cannot be without paine, by reason of their change of place from that which is naturall, into that against nature: none of all which can befall the Kall, seeing it is a stupide body, and almost without sence, heavy, dull, and immoveable. The signes that the *Peritonæum* is broken, are the sudden increase of the tumor, and a sharpe and cutting paine; for when the *Peritonæum* is onely relaxed, the tumor groweth by little and little, and so consequently with small paine; yet such paine returnes so often, as the tumor is renewed by the falling downe of the Gut, or Kall, which happens not the *Peritonæum* being broken: for the way being once open, and passable to the falling body, the tumor is renued without any distention, and so without

The Causes.

The signes.

any paine to speake of. The rest of the signes shall be handled in their places. Sometimes it happens that the Guts, and Kall, do so firmely adhere to the processe of the *Peritonæum*, that they can not be driven back into their proper seate. This stubborne adhesion happens by the intervention of the viscide matter, or by meanes of some excoriation caused by the rude hand of a Chirurgion, in too violently forcing of the Gut, or Kall, into their place. But also, too long stay of the gut in the codde, and the neglect of wearing a Trusse, may give occasion to such adhesion. A perfect and inveterate rupture by the breaking of the processe of the *Peritonæum* in men of full growth, never, or very seldomes admits of cure. But you must note, that by great ruptures of the *Peritonæum*, the Guts may fall into the codde, to the bignesse of a mans head, without much paine and danger of life, because the excrements, as they may easily enter, by reason of the largenesse of the place and rupture, so also they may easily returne.

What rupture is uncurable.

Of the cure of Ruptures.

Because children are very subject to Ruptures, but those truely not fleshy or varicous, but watry, windy, and especially of the Guts, by reason of continuall and painefull crying and coughing: Therefore in the first place we will treate of their cure. Wherefore the Chirurgion, called to restore the Gut which is fallen downe, shall place the child, either on a table, or in a bed, so that his head shall be low, but his buttocks, and thighes higher; then shall he force with his hands by little and little, and gently, the Gut into its proper place; and shall foment the Groine with the astringent fomentation, described in the falling downe of the wombe. Then let him apply this remedy. ℞, *Præscript. decoctionis quantum sufficit, farinæ hordei & fabarum, an.* ℥j, *pulver. Aloes, Mastiches, Myrtyll. & Sarcoco. an.* ℥ss, *Boli Armeni* ℥ij. Let them be incorporated and made a cataplasme according to Art. For the same purpose he may apply *Emplastrum contra Rupturam*: but the chiefe of the

To what ruptures children are subject.

An astringent cataplasme.

cure consists in folded clothes, and Trusses, and ligatures
artificially made, that the restored gut may be contained in
its place, for which purpose he shall keepe the child seated
in his cradle for 30. or 40. dayes, as we mentioned before;
and keepe him from crying, shouting, and coughing. *Aetius*
bids steepe paper 3. dayes in water, and apply it made into
a ball to the groine, the gut being first put up; for that
remedy by 3. dayes adhesion wil keep it from falling down.
But it wil be, as I suppose more effectuall, if the paper be
steeped not in common, but in the astringent water, described in the falling downe of the wombe. Truely I have
healed many by the helpe of such remedies, and have delivered them from the hands of Gelders, which are greedy
of childrens testicles, by reason of the great gaine they
receive from thence. They by a crafty cozenage, perswade
the Parents, that the falling downe of the Gut into the
Codde, is uncurable: which thing notwithstanding, experience convinceth to be false, if so be the cure be performed
according to the forementioned manner, when the *Peritonæum* is onely relaxed, and not broken: for the processe
thereof by which the Gut doth fall as in a steepe way, in
progresse of time and age is straitned and knit together,
whilest also in the meane time the guts grow thicker.

A certaine Chirurgion who deserveth credit, hath told
me that he hath cured many children as thus: He beates
a loadstone into fine powder, and gives it in pappe, and
then hee annointes with hony the Groine, by which the
gut came out, and then strewed it over with fine filings of
iron. He administred this kinde of remedy for ten or twelve
dayes: The part, for other things, being bound up with a
ligature and trusse as was fitting. The efficacie of this
remedy seemeth to consist in this; that the loadstone by
a naturall desire of drawing the iron which is strewed upon
the Groine, joynes to it the fleshy and fatty particles inter-
posed betweene them, by a certaine violent impetuosity,
which on every side pressing and bending the loosenesse of
the *Peritonæum*, yea verily adjoyning themselves to it, in

*Ser. 1. Cap.
24.*

The craft
and
covetousnesse
of Gelders.

Another way
to cure Rup-
tures.

The reason
of this cure.

processe of time by a firme adhesion intercept the passage and falling downe of the Gut or Kall; which may seeme no more abhorring from reason, than that we behold the loadstone it selfe through the thicknesse of a table, to draw iron after it any way. The same Chirurgion affirmed, that he frequently and happily used the following medicine. Hee burnt into ashes in an Oven red Snailes, shut up in an earthen pot, and gave the powder of them to little children in pappe, but to those which were bigger, in broath.

Another medicine.

But we must despaire of nothing in this disease, for the cure may happily proceede in men of full growth, as of fortie yeare old, who have filled the three demensions of the body, as this following relation testifies.

There was a certaine Priest in the Parish of Saint *Andrewes*, called *John Moret*, whose office it was to sing an Epistle with a loud voice as often as the solemnitie of the day, and the thing required. Wherefore seeing he was troubled with the *Enterocele*, he came to me, requiring helpe, saying, he was troubled with a grievous paine, especially then, when he stretched his voice in the Epistle.

A notable History.

When I had seene the bignesse of the *Enterocele*, I perswaded him to get another to serve in his place; so having gotten leave of M. *Curio*, Clearke and Deacon of Divinity, he committed himselfe unto me: I handled him according unto Art, and commanded him he should never goe without a Trusse; and he followed my directions. When I met him some five or sixe yeares after, I asked him how he did, he answered very well, for he was wholly freed from the disease with which he was formerly troubled; which I could not perswade my selfe of, before that I had found that hee had told mee the truth, by the diligent observation of his genitals. But some sixe moneths after, he dying of a Pleurisie, I came to *Curio's* house where hee died, and desired leave to open his body, that I might observe whether nature had done any thing at all in the passage through which the gut fell down. I call God to witnesse, that I found a certaine fatty substance about the processe of

The Figure of a man broken on one side, wearing a Trusse, whose bolster must have three Tuberosities, two on the upper, and one on the lower part; and there must be a hollownesse betweene them in the middest, that they may not too straitly presse the sharebone, and so cause paine. The manner of such a Trusse, I found out not long agoe, and it seemed better and safer than the rest for to hinder the falling downe of the Gut and Kall.

A. *Shewes the shoulder band which is tied before and behinde to the girdle of the Trusse.*
B. *The Trusse.*
C. *The Cavitie left in the midst of the Tuberosities.*

the *Peritonæum* about the bignesse of a little egge, and it did sticke so hard to that place, that I could scarce pull it away without the rending of the neighbouring parts. And

Another Figure of a man having a Rupture on both sides, shewing by what meanes, what kinde of Trusse, and what shoulder-band he must be bound on each groine.

A. *Sheweth the shoulder-band divided in the middest for the putting through of the head.*
B. *The Trusse, with two bolsters, betweene which is a hole for putting through the yard. The forms of both bolsters ought to be the same with the former.*

this was the speedy cause of his cure. But it is most worthy of observation, and admiration, that Nature but a little helped by Art, healeth diseases which are thought incurable. The chiefe of the cure consists in this, that we firmerly stay the gut in its place, after the same manner as these two Figures shew.

We must never despaire in diseases if so be nature be associated by Art.

In the meane time we must not omit diet. We must forbidde the use of all things, which may either relaxe, dilate, or breake the processe of the *Peritonæum*, of which I have already treated sufficiently. Sometimes, but especially in old men, the guts cannot be restored into their place by reason of the quantity of the excrements hardened in them: In this case they must not be too violently forced, but the Patient must be kept in his bed, and lying with his head low, and his knees higher up; let the following Cataplasmes be applied.

A Cataplasme to soften the excrements.

℞. *rad. alth. & lil. ana. ℥ij. seminis lini. & fænug. an. ℥ss, fol. malvæ, viol. & pariet. an. m.* ss. Let them be boiled in faire water, afterwards beaten, and drawne through a searce,[1] adding thereto of new Butter without salt, and oyle of Lillies, as much as shall suffice. Make a Cataplasme in the forme of a liquid pultis. Let it be applied hot to the Codde, and bottome of the belly; by the helpe of this remedy when it had beene applied all night, the guts have not seldome beene seene of themselves, without the hand of a Chirurgion, to have returned into their proper place. The windinesse being resolved, which hindered the going backe of the excrements into another gut, whereby they might be evacuated and expelled. But if the excrements will not goe backe thus, the flatulencies, yet resisting and undiscussed, an emollient and carminative Clyster is to be admitted with a little Chymicall oyle of Turpentine, Dill, Juniper or Fennill. Clysters of Muscadine, oyle of Wallnuts and *Aqua vitæ*, and a small quantitie of any the aforesaid oyles, are good for the same purpose.

Chymicall oyles.

It often happens that the guts cannot yet be restored, because the processe of the *Peritonæum* is not wide enough. For when the excrements are fallen downe with the gut into the codde; they grow hard by little and little, and encrease by the accesse of flatulencies caused by resolution, which cause such a tumor as cannot be put up through that hole, by which a little before it fell downe: whereby it

---

[1] i.e. a sieve or strainer.

happens that by putrifaction of the matter there contained, come inflammations, and a new accesse of paine; and lastly, a vomitting and evacuation of the excrements by the mouth being hindered from the other passage of the fundament. They vulgarly call this affect *Miserere mei.* That you may helpe this symptome, you must rather assay extreame remedies, than suffer the Patient to die by so filthy and loathsome a death. And we must cure it by Chirurgery after this manner following. We will binde the Patient lying on his backe, upon a Table or Bench; then presently make an incision in the upper part of the codde, not touching the substance of the guts; then we must have a silver Cane or Pipe, of the thicknesse of a Goose quill, round, and gibbous in one part thereof, but somewhat hollowed in the other, as is shewed by this following Figure.

The Figure of the Pipe or Cane.

We must put it into the place of the incision, and put it under the production of the *Peritonæum* being cut together with the codde, all the length of the production; that so with a sharpe knife we may divide the processe of the *Peritonæum*, according to that cavity separated from the guts there contained, by the benefit of the Cane in a right line not hurting the guts. When you have made an indifferent incision, the guts must gently be put up into the belly with your fingers, and then so much of the cut *Peritonæum* must be sowed up, as shall seeme sufficient, that by that passage made more straight, nothing may fall into the Codde, after it is cicatrized.

But if there be such abundance of excrements hardned, either by the stay or heate of inflammation, that that incision is not sufficient to force the excrements into their place, the incision must be made longer, your Cane being thrust up towards the belly: so that it may be sufficient for the free regresse of the guts into the belly. Then sow it up as is fit, and the way will be shut up against the falling downe of the guts or kall; the processe of the *Peritonæum* being made more straight, by reason of the suture; for the rest, the wound shall be cured according to Art. But before you undertake this worke, consider diligently whether the strength of the Patient be sufficient, neither attempt any thing before you have foretold, and declared the danger to the Patients friends.

Of the golden Ligature, or the Punctus Aureus, *as they call it.*

The Chirur-
gicall cure
by the
golden Tye.
    If the Rupture will not be cured by all these meanes, by reason of the great solution of the continuity of the relaxt, or broken *Peritonæum*, and the Patient by the consent of his friends there present, is ready to undergoe the danger in hope of recovery; the cure shall be attempted by that which they call the *Punctus Aureus*, or Golden tie.

For which purpose a Chirurgion which hath a skilfull and sure hand, is to be imploied. He shall make an incision about the share bone, into which he shall thrust a Probe like to the Cane, a little before described; and thrust it long wayes under the processe of the *Peritonæum*, and by lifting it up, separate it from the adjoining fibrous, and nervous bodies, to which it adheres; then presently draw aside the spermatique vessels, with the *Cremaster*, or hanging muscle of the testicle; which being done, he shall draw aside the processe it selfe, alone by it selfe: And he shall take as much thereof, as is too lax, with small and gentle mullets, perforated in the middest, and shall with a needle, having five or sixe threeds, thrust it through as neere as hee can to the spermaticke vessels, and cremaster muscles. But the needle also must be drawne againe into the middest of the remnant of the processe, taking up with it the lipps of the wound; then the threed must be tied on a strait knot, and so much thereof must be left after the section, as may be sufficient to hang out of the wound. This threed will of it selfe be dissolved by little and little by putrefaction: neither must it be drawne out before that nature shall regenerate and restore flesh into the place of the ligature, otherwise all our labour shall be spent in vaine.

And lastly, let the wound be clensed, filled with flesh, and cicatrized, whose callous hardnesse may withstand the falling of the gut, or kall.

There are some Chirurgians who would performe this golden Ligature after another manner. They cut the skinne above the share-bone where the falling downe commonly is, even to the processe of the *Peritonæum*, and they wrap once or twice about it, being uncovered, a small golden wyre, and onely straiten the passage as much as may suffice, to amend the loosenesse of this processe, leaving the spermatique vessels at liberty. Then they twist the ends of the wyre twice or thrice with small mullets, and cut off the remnant thereof; that which remaines after the cutting, they turne in, least with the sharpnesse it should prick the flesh growing upon it. Then leaving the golden wyre there, they cure the wound like to other simple wounds, and they keepe the Patient some fifteene or twenty day in his bed, with his knees some thing higher, and his head some thing lower.

Another manner thereof.

Many are healed by this meanes; others have fallen againe into the disease by reason of the ill twisting of the wire.

There is also another manner of this golden tie, which I judge more quicke and safe, even for that there is no externall body left in that part after the cure. Wherefore they wrappe a leaden wyre in steade of the golden, which comes but once about the processe of the *Peritonæum*, then they twine it as much as neede requires, that is, not too loosely, least it should leave way for the falling downe of the body, neither too straitly, least a Gangrene should come by hindring the passage of the spirits and nourishment. The ends thereof are suffered to hang out; when in processe of

The third manner thereof.

time, this contraction of the *Peritonæum* seemes callous,
then the wyre is untwisted and gently drawne out. And
the rest of the cure performed according to Art. But let

A thing to
be noted.

not the Chirurgion thrust himselfe upon his worke rashly,
without the advice of the Physition, for it diverse times
comes to passe, that the testicles are not as yet fallen downe
into the Codde by the too great sluggishnesse of nature, in
some of a pretty growth, but remaines long in the groines,
causing a tumor with paine, which thing may make a good
Chirurgion beleeve that it is an *Enterocele.* Therefore whilst
he labours by repelling medicines and trusses to force backe
this tumor, he encreaseth the paine, and hinders the falling
downe of the testicles into the codde. I observed this not

A History.

long agoe in a Boy, which an unskilfull Chirurgion had
long, and grievously troubled, as if he had had a rupture:
for when I had observed that there was but one stone in
the Codde, and knew the Boy was never gelt, I bid them
cast away the plasters, and trusses, and wisht his Parents
that they should suffer him to run and leape, that so the
idleing stone might be drawne into the Codde, which thing
by little and little, and without paine, had the event, as I
foretold. That the reason of this effect may be understood,
we must know a man differs from a woman, onely in
efficacie of heat; but it is the nature of strong heat to drive
forth, as of cold to keepe in. Hence it is that the stones in
men hang forth in the codde, but in women they lie hid
in the lower belly. Therefore it happens that in some males
more cold by nature, the testicles are shut up some certaine
time, untill at length they are forc'st downe into the codde
by youthfull heat. But that we may returne to our former
treatise of the codde, although that way of curing ruptures
wants not paine and danger, yet it is safer than that which
is performed by gelding, which by the cruelty thereof
exposes the Patient to manifest danger of death. For the
Gelders whilst they feare least when the cure is finshed, the
relaxation may remaine, pull with violence the processe of
the *Peritonæum* from the parts to which it adheres, and

together with it a nerve of the sixth conjugation which runnes to the stones; they offer the same violence to the spermaticke vessels; by which things ensue great paine, convulsion, effluxe of bloud, inflammation, putrefaction,

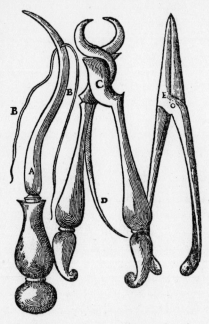

A. *Shewes a croked needle, having an eye not farre from the point, through which you may put the golden wyre.*

B.B. *The golden wyre put through the eye of the needle.*

C. *The mullets or Pincers, to cut away the wast or superfluous ends of the wyre.*

D. *The springe of the mullets.*

E. *The mullets to twist the ends of the wyre together.*

and lastly death, as I have observed in many whom I have dissected, having died a few dayes after their gelding. Although some escape these dangers, yet they are deprived of the faculty of generation for all their life after, for performance whereof nature hath bestowed the testicles, as parts principally necessary for the conservation of

Lib. de arte medica.

mankinde. Through which occasion *Galen* hath not feared to preferre them before the heart; because the heart is the beginning of life, but the testicles of a better life; for it is farre more noble to live well, than simply and absolutely

Lib. de fem.

to live; therefore Eunuches degenerate into a womanish nature, for they remaine without beards, their voice is weake, their courage failes them, and they turne cowards; and seeing they are unfit for all humane actions, their life cannot but be miserable. Wherefore I will never subscribe to the cutting out of the stones, unlesse a *Sarcocele* or Gangrene invade them. But that the way of performing the *Punctus aureus* may be better knowne, I have thought good here to set the instruments, by which this operation is performed, before your view.

Another more easie and safe way to restore the Gut and Kall.

Lib. 3, Cap. 33.

Theodoricke and *Guido* have invented another way of performing this operation. They put backe into their places the Gut and Kall being fallen downe, the Patient being so placed, that his thighs are high and his head is somewhat low; then they draw aside the lower portion of the production of the *Peritonæum*, and also the spermaticke vessels, and cremaster muscle to the *Ischium*; then by applying a causticke fitted to the age and disease, they burne the other part of the processe, directly perpendicular to the share-bone, where the Gut did fall downe. Then they pull off the eschar thus made with a knife even to the quicke, then they apply another causticke in the same place, which may go even to the bone, then procure the falling of this Eschar made on the foresaid processe. And afterwards they heale the ulcer which remaines, which presently contracting somewhat, a thicke *Callus* so keeps up the Guts and Kall, that it bindes them from falling down into the Cod. This way of restoring the Gut and Kall, though it be safer and more facile; yet the Chirurgion must not attempt it, if the Guts or Kall sticke so fast, agglutinated to the processe of the *Peritonæum*, that they cannot be severed, nor put backe into their places (for from the guts so burnt and violated, greater mischiefe would ensue) if by the broken and too much dilated processe, the bodies thereby restrained, make an exceeding great tumor by their falling downe; if the testicle yet lying in the groine as in a *Bubonocele*, a kinde of *Enterocele*, being not yet descended into the *Scrotum* or Codde; if the Patients be not come to such age as they can keepe themselves from stirring, or hold their excrements whiles the operation is performed.

Of the cure of other kinds of Ruptures.

Epiplocele is the falling downe of the Kall into the Groine, or Codde, it hath the same causes as an *Enterocele*. The signes have beene explained. It is not so dangerous, nor infers a consequence of so many evill symptomes, as the *Enterocele* doth, yet the cure is the same with the other.

Hydrocele is a waterish tumor in the Codde, which is gathered by little and little betweene the membranes encompassing the testicles, especially the *Dartos* and *Erythroides*; it may be called a particular dropsie, for it proceeds from the same causes, but chiefly from the defect of native heate. The signes are a tumor encreasing slowly without much paine, heavy, and almost of a glassie clearenesse, which you may perceive by holding a candle on the other side, by pressing the Codde above, the water flowes downe, and by pressing it below, it rises upwards, unlesse peradventure in too great a quantity it fills up the whole capacity of the Codde, yet it can never be forced or put up into the belly as the Kall or Guts may, for oft times it is contained in a Cyste, or bagge; it is distinguished from a *Sarcocele*, by the smoothnesse and equality thereof. The cure must first be tried with resolving, drying, and discussing medicines, repeated often before, and in the Chapter of the Dropsie; this which followes I have often tried with good successe.

℞, *Ung. comitissæ, & desiccat. rub. an. ℥ ij. malaxentur simul;* and make a medicine for your case. The water by this kinde

What a Hydrocele is.

The signes.

The cure.

A medicine to draw forth the contained matter.

of remedy is digested and resolved, or rather dried up, especially if it be not in too great quantity. But if the swelling, by reason of the great quantity of water will not yeeld to those remedies, there is neede of Chirurgery; the Cod and membranes wherein the water is contained, must be thrust through with a Seton, that is, with a large three-square pointed needle, thred with a skeane of silke; you must thrust your needle presently through the holes of the mullets made for that purpose, not touching the substance of the Testicles. The skean of thred must be left there, or removed twise or thrise a day, that the humor may drop downe, and be evacuated by little and little. But if the paine be more vehement by reason of the Seton, and inflammation come upon it, it must be taken away, and neglecting the proper cure of the disease, we must resist the symptomes.

Some Practitioners use not a Seton, but with a Razor, or incision knife, they open the lower part of the Cod, making an incision some halfe fingers breadth long, penetrating even to the contained water; always leaving untouched the substance of the Testicles and vessels, and they keepe the wound open, untill all the water seemes evacuated; truly by this onely way the cure of a watery rupture whose matter is contained in a Cyste, is safe, and to be expected; as wee have said in our Treatise of Tumors in generall.

What a *Pneumatocele* is.

The *Pneumatocele*, is a flatulent tumor in the Codde, generated by the imbecility of heate residing in the part.

The Cure.

It is knowne by the roundnesse, lenity, renitencie[1] and shining. It is cured by prescribing a convenient diet, by the application of medicines which resolve and discusse flatulencies, as the seeds of Annis, Fennell, Fænugreeke, *Agnus Castus*, Rue, *Origanum*, other things set downe by *Avicen* in his Treatise of Ruptures. I have often used with good successe for this purpose, *Emplastrum Vigonis cum mercurio*; and *Emplastrum Diacalcitheos*, dissolved in some good wine, as Muscadine, with oyle of Bayes.

[1] i.e. resistance.

A *Sarcocele* is a tumor against nature, which is generated about the stones by a schyrrhus flesh. Grosse and viscide humors breed such kind of flesh, which the part could not overcome and assimulate to it selfe; whence this over-abundance of flesh proceeds, like as Warts doe. *Varices*, or swollen veines often associate this tumor; and it increases with paine. It is knowne by the hardnesse, asperitie, in-equality, and roughnesse. It cannot be cured but by am-putation or cutting it away; but you must diligently observe, that the flesh be not growne too high, and have already seazed upon the Groine, for so nothing can be attempted without the danger of life.

But if any may thinke, that he in such a case may some-what ease the patient by the cutting away of some portion of this same soft flesh, he is deceived. For a *Fungus* will grow, if the least portion thereof be but left, being an evill farre worse than the former; but if the tumor be either small or indifferent, the Chirurgion taking the whole tumor, that is, the testicle, tumefied through the whole substance, with the processe encompassing it, and adhering thereto on every side, and make an incision in the Codde, even to the tumor; then separate all the tumid body, that is, the testicle from the Codde; then let him thrust a needle with a strong threed in it, through the middest of the pro-cesse above the region of the swolne testicle; and then presently let him thrust it the second time through the same part of the processe; then shall both the ends of the threed be tied on a knot, the other middle portion of the *Peritonæum* being comprehended in the same knot. This being done, he must cut away the whole processe with the testicle comprehended therein. But the ends of the threed, with which the upper part of the processe was bound, must be suffered to hang some length out of the wound, or incision of the Codde. Then a repercussive medicine shall be applied to the wound, and the neighbouring parts with a convenient ligature. And the cure must be performed as we have formerly mentioned.

What a *Sarcocele* is.

The signes.
Prognosticks.

The cure.

What a
Cirsocele is.

The *Cirsocele* is a tumor of veines dilated, and woven with a various and mutuall implication about the testicle and codde, and swelling with a grosse and melancholy bloud. The causes are the same as those of the *Varices*. But the signes are manifest.

The Cure.

To heale this tumor, you must make an incision in the codde, the bredth of two fingers to the *Varix*. Then you must put under the varicous veine, a needle having a double threed in it, as high as you can, that you may binde the rootes thereof: then let the needle be againe put after the same manner about the lower part of the same veine, leaving the space of two fingers betweene the Ligatures. But before you binde the thread of this lowest Ligature, the *Varix* must bee opened in the middest, almost after the same manner as you open a veine in the arme to let bloud: That so this grosse blood causing a tumor in the Cod, may be evacuated as is usually done in the Cure of the *varices*. The wound that remaines shall be cured by the rules of Art after the manner of other wounds: Leaving the threads in it, which will presently fall away of themselves. To conclude then, it being growne callous especially in the upper part thereof, where the veine was bound, it must be Cicatrized, for so afterwards the bloud cannot be strained, or run that way.

*Hernia
Humoralis.*

Hernia Humoralis is a tumor generated by the confused mixture of many humors in the Cod or betweene the tunicles which involue the testicles, often also in the proper substance of the testicles. It hath like causes, signes and cure as other tumors. While the cure is in hand, rest, trusses, and fit rowlers to sustaine and beare up the testicles are to be used.

OF WOUNDS
IN GENERALL

What a Wound is, what the kindes and differences thereof are,
and from whence they may be drawne, or derived.

WOUND is a solution of Continuity, caused by a stroake, fall, or bite, newly done, bloody, and with putrifaction, and filth. They also call it a new simple ulcer; for the solution of continuity happens to all parts of the body; but according to the diversity of the parts, it hath divers names amongst the Greekes. For in the flesh it is called *Helcos*, in the bone *Catagma*, in the nerve *Spasma*, in the ligament *Thlasma*, in the vesselles *Apospasma*, in the Muscles *Regma*: and that solution of continuity, which happens in the vessells, their mouths being open, is termed *Anastomosis*, that which happens by erosion, *Anaurosis*; that which is generated by sweating out and transcolation, *Diapedesis*. That these may bee the more easily understood, I have thought good to describe them in the table on p. 118.

What a Wound properly is.

Divers appellations of wounds according to the varieties of the parts.

Of the causes of Wounds.

All things which may outwardly assayle the body with force and violence, may be counted the causes of wounds; which are called greene, and properly bloody. These things are either animate, or inanimate. The animate, as the bitings, and prickings of beasts. The Inanimate, as the stroake of an arrow, sword, clubb, gunne, stone, a dagger, and all such like things.

From the variety of such like causes, they have divers

Divers denominations from their causes.

A Table of the differences of Wounds.

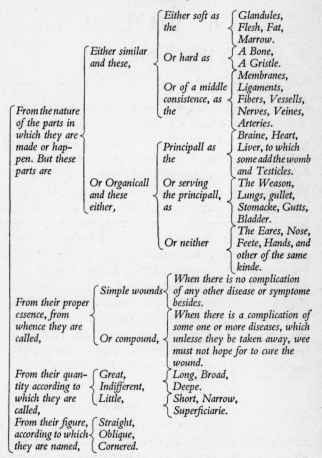

The differences of wounds
are drawn or taken,

From the nature of the parts in which they are made or happen. But these parts are

Either similar and these,

Either soft as the — Glandules, Flesh, Fat, Marrow.

Or hard as — A Bone, A Gristle.

Or of a middle consistence, as the — Membranes, Ligaments, Fibers, Vessells, Nerves, Veines, Arteries.

Or Organicall and these either,

Principall as the — Braine, Heart, Liver, to which some add the womb and Testicles.

Or serving the principall, as — The Weason, Lungs, gullet, Stomacke, Gutts, Bladder.

Or neither — The Eares, Nose, Feete, Hands, and other of the same kinde.

From their proper essence, from whence they are called,

Simple wounds — When there is no complication of any other disease or symptome besides.

Or compound, — When there is a complication of some one or more diseases, which unlesse they be taken away, wee must not hope for to cure the wound.

From their quantity according to which they are called,

Great, — Long, Broad, Deepe.

Indifferent,

Little, — Short, Narrow, Superficiarie.

From their figure, according to which they are named,

Straight, Oblique, Cornered.

names: for those which are made by sharpe and pricking things are called punctures: those caused by cutting things, are called wounds or gashes: and those which are made by heavy and obtuse things are named Contusions, or wounds with Contusions.

Of the signes of Wounds.

Wounds are first knowne by sight, and by the signes drawne from thence. The Chirurgion ought first and chiefely, to consider, what wounds are cureable, and what not; what wounds will scarce admit of cure, and what may be easily cured; for it is not the part of a prudent Chirurgion, to promise cure in a deadly or dangerous and difficult wound; Least he may seeme to have killed him, whom not the unsufficiencie of the Art, but the greatnesse of the wound hath slaine. *A caution for making reports of Wounds.*

But when the wound is dangerous, but yet without despaire of recovery, it belongs to him to admonish the Patients friends which are by, of the present danger, and doubtfull state of the wound; that if Art shall be overcome by the greatnesse thereof, hee shall not be thought ignorant of the Art, neither to have deceived them.

But as this is the part and duty of a good and prudent Chirurgion, so it is the tricke of a cheating and jugling knave, to enlarge small wounds, that so he may seeme to have done a great cure, when it is nothing so. *A Jugling cheating Chirurgion.*

But it is agreeable to reason, that the Chirurgion professing the disease easie to be cured, will thinke himselfe in credit bound by such promises and his duty, and therefore seeke all meanes for the quicke recovery of the patient; lest that which was of its owne nature small, may by his negligence become great. Therefore it is expedient, he should know what wounds are to be accounted great.

This (as *Galen* saith) is three wayes to be knowne; The first is by the magnitude and principallity of the part affected; for thus the wounds of the Braine, Heart, and of the greater vessells, though small of themselves, yet are thought great. Then from the greatnesse of the solution of continuity; for which cause wounds may be judged great, in which much of the substance of the part is lost in every dimension, though the part be one of these which are accounted servile. Then from the malignitie; through *Lib.* 4. *Meth. cap.* 6, 1.

Wounds are called great out of three respects.

which occasion the wounds of the joynts are accounted great, because for the most part, they are ill conditioned.

Of Prognostickes to be made in Wounds.

What
wounds are
dangerous.

Those Wounds are thought dangerous, wherein any large Nerve, Veine, or Artery are hurt. From the first there is feare of convulsion, but from the other large effusion of the veinous, or arterious blood, whence the powers are debilitated; also these are judged evill, which are upon the arme pitts, groines, leskes,[1] joynts and betweene the fingers; and likewise those which hurt the head or taile of a Muscle. They are least dangerous of all other which wound onely the fleshy substance. But they are deadly which are inflicted

What least
dangerous.
What deadly.
Hip. aphor.
19. *Lib.* 6.

upon the Bladder, Braine, Heart, Liver, Lungs, Stomacke and small guts. But if any Bone, Gristle, Nerve or portion of the cheeke or prepuce, shall be cut away, they cannot bee restored. Contused wounds are more difficult to cure, than those which are onely from a simple solution of continuity; for before you must thinke to heale them up, you must suppurate and clense them; which cannot be done in a short time. Wounds which are round and circular are so much the worse; for there can be no unity unlesse by an angle, that is, a meeting together of two lines, which can

Why round
Wounds are
difficult to
heale.

have no place in round wounds, because a circular figure consists of one oblique line. Besides, wounds are by so much thought the greater, by how much their extremes and lipps are the further dis-joyned, which happens to round Wounds. Contrary to these are cornered wounds or such as are made alongst the fibers, as such as may bee easily healed.

Wounds may be more easily healed in young men, than in old, because in them nature is more vigorous, and there is a greater plenty of fruitefull, or good blood, by which the losse of the flesh may be the better and more readily restored, which is slowlier done in an old body, by reason

---

[1] A variant of lisk, i.e. flank or loin.

their blood is smaller in quantity and more dry, and the strength of nature more languide.

Wounds received in the Spring, are not altogether so difficult to heale as those taken in Winter or Summer. For all excesse of heate and cold is hurtfull to them; it is ill for a convulsion to happen upon a Wound, for it is a signe that some Nervous body is hurt; the braine suffering together therewith, as that which is the originall of the Nerves. A Tumor comming upon great Wounds is good; for it shewes the force of nature is able to expell that which is harmefull, and to ease the wounded part. The organicall parts wholly cut off cannot againe be united: because a vitall part once severed and plucked from the trunke of the body cannot any more receive influence from the heart as from a roote without which there can bee no life. The loosed continuity of the Nerves, Veines, Arteries, and also the bones, is sometimes restored, not truely, and as they say, according to the first intention, but by the second, that is, by reposition of the like, but not of the same substance. The first intention takes place in the fleshie parts by converting the Alimentary bloud into the proper substance of the wounded part. But the second, in the spermatique parts in which the lost substance may be repaired by interposition of some heterogeneous body, which nature, diligent for its owne preservation, substitutes in place of that which is lost: for thus the body, which restores and agglutinats, is no bone but a *Callus*, whose originall matter is from an humor somewhat grosser than that, from whence the bones have their originall and beginning.

This humor, when it shall come to the place of the fracture, agglutinateth the ends of the bones together, which otherwise could never bee so knit by reason of their hardnesse. The bones of children are more easily and speedily united by reason of the pliantnesse of their soft and tender substance. Lastly wee must here admonish the Chirurgion, that small Wounds and such as no Artisan will judge deadly, doe divers times kill by reason of a certaine occult

Hip. lib. de ulcer. Hip. aph. 66, lib. 5.

What a *Callus* is and whence it proceedes.

Small and contemptible Wounds often prove mortall.

and ill disposition of the wounded, and incompassing bodies; for which cause we reade it observed by *Hippocrates*, that it is not sufficient for the Physition to performe his duty, but also externall things must be rightly prepared, and fitted.

Of the Cure of Wounds in generall.

The Chirurgion ought for the right cure of wounds to propose unto himselfe the common and generall indication: that is, the uniting of the divided parts, which indication in such a case is thought upon and knowne even by the vulgar: for that which is dis-joyned desires to bee united, because union is contrary to division. But by what meanes such union may be procured, is onely knowne to the skilfull Artisan. Therefore we attaine unto this chiefe and principall Indication by the benefit of nature as it were the chiefe Agent, and the work of the Chirurgion as the servant of nature. And unlesse nature shall be strong the Chirurgion shall never attaine to his conceived, and wished for end: therefore that he may attaine hereto, he must performe five things; the first is, that if there bee any strange bodies, as peeces of Wood, Iron, Bones, bruised flesh, congealed blood, or the like, whether they have come from without, or from within the body, and shall be by accident fastened or stucke in the wound, he must take them away, for otherwise there is no union to be expected.

Another is, that he joyne together the lippes of the Wound; for they cannot otherwise be agglutinated and united. The third is, that he keepe close together the joyned lippes. The fourth, that he preserve the temper of the wounded part, for the distemper remaining, it is impossible to restore it to its unity. The fifth is, that he correct the accidents, if any shall happen, because these urging, the Physition is often forced to change the order of the cure.

All strange and externall bodies must bee taken away, as speedily as is possible, because they hinder the action of nature intending unity, especially if they presse or pricke any Nervous body, or Tendon, whence paine or an Abscesse may breede in any principall part, or other serving the principall.

Yet if by the quicke and too hasty taking forth of such like bodies there bee feare of cruell paine or great effusion of bloud, it will bee farre better to commit the whole worke to nature than to exasperate the Wound by too violent hastening.

For nature by little and little will exclude, as contrary to it, or else together with the *Pus*, what strange body soever shall be contayned in the wounded part. But if there shall be danger in delay, it will bee fit the Chirurgion fall to worke quickely, safely, and as mildely as the thing will suffer: for effusion of blood, swooning, convulsion and other horrid symptomes, follow upon the too rough and boystrous handling of Wounds, whereby the patient shall be brought into greater danger than by the wound it selfe.

Therefore he may pull out the strange bodies, either with his fingers, or with instruments, fit for that purpose: but they are sometimes more easily and sometimes more hardly pulled forth, according as the body infixed is either hard or easie to be found or pulled out. Which thing happens according to the variety of the figure of such like bodies; according to the condition of the part it selfe, soft, hard, or deepe, in which these bodies are fastened more straitly or more loosely; and then for feare of inferring any worse harme, as the breaking of some Vessell; but how wee may performe this first intention, and also the expression of the instruments necessary for this purpose, shall be showne in the particular treaties of wounds made by Gun-shot, Arrowes and the like.

But the Surgeon shall attaine to the second and third scope of curing wounds by two and the same meanes, that is, by ligatures and sutures: which notwithstanding before hee use, hee must well observe whether there be any great fluxe of blood present, for he shall stoppe it if it be too violent; but provoake it, if too slow, (unlesse by chance it

Ligatures and Sutures for to conjoyne and hold together the lippes of wounds.

shall be powred out into any capacity or belly) that so the part freed from the superfluous quantity of blood may be lesse subject to inflammation. Therefore the lippes of the wounds shall be put together, and shall bee kept so joyned by suture and ligatures: Not truly of all, but onely of those which both by their nature, and magnitude, as also by the condition of the parts in which they are, are worthy and capable of both the remedies. For a simple and small solution of continuity, stands only in neede of the Ligature which we call incarnative, especially, if it be in the Armes or Legges; but that which divides the Muscles transversly, stands in need of both Suture and Ligature; that so the Lippes which are somewhat farre distant from each other, and as it were drawne towards their beginnings, and ends, may bee conjoyned.

If any portion of a fleshy substance by reason of some great cut shall hang downe, it must necessarily be adjoyned and kept in the place by suture. The more notable and large Wounds of all the parts, stand in need of Suture, which doe not easily admit a Ligature, by reason of the figure and site of the part in which they are, as the Eares, Nose, Hairy-scalpe, Eie-liddes, Lippes, Belly and Throat.

Three sorts of Ligatures:

There are three sorts of Ligatures, by the joynt consent of all the Ancients. They commonly call the first, a Gluti-native or Incarnative; the second Expulsive, the third Retentive. The Glutinative or Incarnative is fit for simple, greene, and yet bloody wounds. This consists of two ends, and must so be drawne, that beginning on the contrary part of the wound, wee may so goe upwards, partly crossing it, and going downewards againe, we may closely joyne together the lippes of the Wound. But let the Ligature be neither too strait, least it may cause inflammation or paine; nor too loose, least it be of no use, and may not well containe it.

What an incarnative Ligature is.

What an expulsive.

The Expulsive Ligature is fit for sanious and fistulous ulcers, to presse out the filth contained in them. This is performed with one Rowler, having one simple head; the beginning of binding must bee taken from the bottome of the *Sinus*, or bosome thereof; and there it must be bound more straightly, and so by little and little going higher, you must remit something of that rigour, even to the mouth of the Ulcer. That so (as we have said) the sanious matter may be pressed forth.

The Retentive Ligature is fit for such parts as cannot suffer straight binding, such are the Throat, Belly, as also all parts oppressed with paine; For the part vexed with paine, abhorreth binding. The use thereof, is to hold to locall Medicines. It is performed with a Rowler, which consists some whiles of one, some whiles of more heads. All these Rowlers ought to be of linnen, and such as is neither too new, nor too old; neither too coarse, nor too fine. Their breadth must be proportionable to the parts to which they shall bee applyed; the indication of their largenesse being taken from their magnitude, figure and site. As wee shall shew more at large in our Tractates of Fractures and Dislocations.

The Chirurgion shall performe the first scope of curing Wounds, which is of preserving the temper of the Wounded part, by appointing a good order of Diet by the Prescript of a Physition, by using universall and locall Medicines. A slender, cold, and moyst Diet must be observed, untill that time be passed, wherein the patient may be safe and free from accidents which are usually feared. Therefore let him bee fed sparingly, especially if he be plethorick; he shall abstaine from salt and spiced flesh, and also from wine; If he shall be of a Cholerick or Sanguine nature: In steed of wine he shall use the decoction of Barly or Liquerice, or Water and Sugar. He shall keepe himselfe quiet; for rest is (in *Celsus* opinion) the very best Medicine. Hee shall avoyde Venery, Contentions, Brawles, Anger, and other perturbations of the minde. When hee shall seeme to bee past danger, it will bee time to fall by little and little to his accustomed maner of diet and life. Universall remedies are Phlebotomies and purging, which have force to divert and

[marginal notes:]
What the retentive.

What the rowlers must bee made of.

Why and how the temper of the wounded part must be preserved.

hinder defluxion, wherby the temper of the part might be in danger of change.

In what
wounds
blood letting
is not neces-
sary.

For Phlebotomy it is not alwayes necessary, as in small wounds and bodies, which are neither troubled with ill humours, nor plethoricke: But it is onely required in great wounds, where there is feare of defluxion, paine, *Delirium*, Raving and unquietnesse; and lastly in a body that is Plethoricke, and when the joynts, tendons, or nerves are wounded. Gentle purgations must bee appointed, because the humours are moved and inraged by stronger; whence there is danger of defluxion and inflammation: wherefore nothing is to be attempted in this case, without the advice of a Physition.

What medi-
cines are to
be judged
agglutina-
tive.

The Topick and particular Medicines are Agglutinative, which ought to be indued with a drying and astrictive quality, whereby they may hold together the lips of the wound, and drive away defluxion, having alwayes regard to the nature of the part and the greatnesse of the disease. The Simple Medicines are *Olibanum*, *Aloes*, *Sarcocolla*, *Bole-Armenick*, *Terra sigillata*, *Sanguis Draconis*, Common and Venice Turpentine, Gumme *Elemnii*, Plantane, Horse-tayle, the greater Comfery, *Farina Volatilis*, and many other things of this kind, which wee shall speake of hereafter in our Antidotary.

The fifth scope of healing wounds, is the Correction of those Symptomes or Accidents which are accustomed to follow wounds, which thing verily makes the Chirurgion have much to doe; For he is often forced to omit the proper cure of the disease, so to resist the accidents and symptomes, as bleeding, paine, inflammation, a feaver, convulsion, palsie, talking idly, or distraction, and the like. Of which wee shall treat briefly and particularly, after we have first spoken of Sutures as much as we shall thinke fitting for this place.

What
wounds
stand in
need of a
suture.

Of Sutures.

When Wounds are made alongst the thighes, Legs, and armes, they may easily want Sutures, because the solution of continuity is easily restored by Ligatures, but when they are made overthwart, they require a Suture, because the flesh and all such like parts, being cut are drawne towards the sound parts; whereby it comes to passe that they part the further each from other; wherefore that they may be joyned and so kept, they must be sowed, and if the wound be deepe, you must take up much flesh with your needle; for if you onely take hold of the upper part, the wound is onely superficially healed: but the matter shut up, and gathered together in the bottome of the wound, will cause abscesses and hollow Ulcers: Wherefore now wee must treate of making of Sutures.

The first, called *Interpunctus*, leaves the distance of a fingers breadth, and therfore is fit for the greene wounds of the fleshy parts, which cannot be cured with a Ligature, and in which no heterogeneous or strange body remaines; It is performed after this manner. You must have a smooth needle with a threed in it, having a three square point, that so it may the better enter the skin, with the head of it some what hollowed, that the threed may lie therein; for so the needle will the better goe through. You must also have a little pipe with a hole or window in the end, which you must hold and thrust against the lip of the wound, that it bee not moved to the one side or other, whilest you thrust thorough the needle. And that wee may see thorough that window when the needle is thrust thorough, and also draw it together with the threed, and withall hold the lip of the wound in more firmly, that it follow not at the drawing forth of the needle and threed. Having thus pierced the lips of the wound, tie a knot, neere to which cut off the threed; least that if any of it bee left below the knot, it may so stick to the Emplasters that it cannot be plucked and separated from them without paine, when they are taken off. But you must note, the first stitch must be thrust through the midst of the wound, and then the second must be in that space which is betweene the midst and one of the ends; but when you have made your stitches, the lips of

The first manner of suture.

The forme of your needle.

The forme of the pipe, with a window in it.

the wound must not be too closely joyned, but a little space must be left open betweene them, that the matter may have free passage forth, and the inflammation and paine may be avoyded: otherwise if they shall be closely joyned together without any distance betweene, a tumor after arising when the matter shall come to suppuration, the lips will be so much distended that they may easily be broken by the stiffnesse of the threed. But you must neither take hold of too much nor too little flesh with your needle, for too little

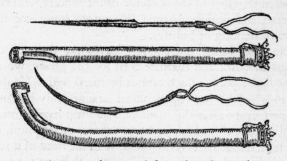

The Figure of Pipes with fenestrels in them, and
Needles fit for Sutures.

will not hold, and too much causeth paine and inflammation. And besides leaves an ill favoured scarre. Yet in deepe wounds, such as are those which are made in the thicker Muscles, the needle must be thrust home, that so it may comprehend more of the fleshy substance; least the thred drawne away by the weight of the flesh not taken hold of, may bee broken. But oft times wounds are seene made in such places as it will be needfull, the Chirurgion should have a crooked needle and pipe, otherwise the Suture will not succeede according to his desire. Wherefore I have thought good to set forth both their figures, that you may use either as occasion shall serve.

The 2. maner of Suture.

The second Suture is made just after the same manner as the Skinners sowe their fels or furrs. And the guts must be sowed with this kind of Suture, (if they shall be at any time wounded) that the excrements come not forth by the wound.

The third Suture is made by one or more needles having threed in them, thrust through the wound, the threed being wrapped to and againe at the head and the point of the needle, as boyes use to fasten their needle, for feare of losing it, in their caps, or clothes. This kind of Suture is fit in the curing and healing of Hare-lips. *The third manner of Suture.*

The fourth kind of Suture is tearmed *Gastroraphia*, invented for the restoring and uniting the great Muscles of the *Epigastrium*, or lower belly, cut with a great wound together with the *Peritonæum* lying under them. *The 4. kind of Suture termed Gastroraphia.*

The fifth kind is called the Dry Suture, which we use onely in the wounds of the face. *The 5. kind called the Dry Suture.*

OF WOUNDS
MADE BY GUNSHOT, OTHER
FIERIE ENGINES, AND
ALL SORTS OF WEAPONS

The Preface.

I HAVE thought good here to premise my opinion of the originall, encrease, and hurt of fiery Engines, for that, I hope it will be an ornament and grace to this my whole treatise: as also to intice my Reader, as it were with these junckets, to our following Banquet so much savouring of Gunpouder. For thus it shall bee knowne to all whence Guns had their originall, and how many habits and shapes they have acquired from poore and obscure beginnings, and lastly how hurtfull to mankind the use of them is.

Lib. 2. *de invent. rerum.* *Polydore Virgill* writes that a Germane of obscure birth and condition was the inventor of this new engine which we terme a Gun, being induced thereto by this occasion. He kept in a mortar covered with a tyle, or slate, for some other certaine uses a pouder (which since that time for its chiefe and new knowne faculty, is named Gunpouder.) Now it chanced as hee strucke fire with a steele and flint, a sparke thereof by accident fell into the mortar, whereupon the pouder suddainly catching fire, casts the stone or tyle which covered the mortar, up on high; he stood amazed at the novelty and strange effect of the thing, and withall observed the formerly unknowne faculty of the pouder; so that he thought good to make experiment thereof in a small Iron trunke framed for that purpose according to the intention of his minde. When all things were correspondent to his expectation, he first shewed the use of his engine to the Venetians, when they warred with the Genoveses about *Fossa Clodia*, in the yeare of our Lord 1380. Yet in the opinion of *Peter Messias*,[1] their invention must have beene of greater antiquity; for it is read in the Chronicles of *Alphonsus* the eleaventh King of *Castile*, who subdued the Isles *Argezires*, that when he beseiged the cheefe Towne in the yeare of our Lord 1343. the beseiged Moores shot as it were thunder against the assailants, out of Iron mortars. But we have read in the Chronicles written by *Peter* Bishop of *Leons*, of that *Alphonsus* who conquered *Toledo*, that in a certaine sea fight fought by the King of *Tunis*, against the Moorish King of *Sivill*, whose part King *Alphonsus* favoured, the *Tunetans* cast lightning out of certaine hollow Engines or Trunkes with much noise. Which could be no other, than our Guns, though not attained to that perfection of art and execution which they now have.

Cap. 8. prim. part. var. lect.

I thinke the deviser of this deadly Engine hath this for his recompence, that his name should be hidden by the darkenesse of perpetuall ignorance, as not meriting for this his most pernicious invention, any mention from posterity. Yet *Andrew Thevet* in his Cosmography[2] published some few yeares agone, when hee comes to treate of the *Suevi*, the inhabitants of Germany, brings upon the authority & credite of a certaine old Manuscript, that the Germane the inventer of this warlike Engine was by profession a monke and Philosopher or Alchymist, borne at *Friburge*, and named *Constantine Ancken*. Howsoever it was, this kind of Engine was called *Bombarda* i.e. a Gun, from that noise it makes, which the Greekes and Latines according to the sound call *Bombus*: then in the following ages, time, art and mans maliciousnesse added much to this rude and unpolisht

Who the inventor of Guns.

The reason of the name.

---

[1] Pedro Mexia.
[2] *Cosmographie Universelle*, Paris, 1575, vol. II, p. 919.

invention. For first for the matter, Brasse and Copper, mettalls farre more tractable, fusible and lesse subject to rust, came as supplies to Iron. Then for the forme, that rude and undigested barrell, or mortar-like masse, hath undergone many formes and fashions, even so farre as it is gotten upon wheeles, that so it might run not onely from the higher ground, but also with more rapide violence to the ruine of mankinde; when as the first and rude mortars seemed not to bee so nimbly traversed, nor sufficiently cruell for our destruction by the onely casting forth of Iron & fire. Hence sprung these horrible monsters of Canons, double Canons, Bastards, Musquits, feild peices; hence these cruell and furious beasts, Culverines, Serpentines, Basilisques, Sackers, Falcons, Falconets, and divers other names not onely drawne from their figure and making, but also from the effects of their cruelty. Wherefore certainly I cannot sufficiently admire the wisedome of our Ancestors, who have so rightly accommodated them with names agreeable to their natures; as those who have not onely taken them from the swiftest birds of prey, as Falcons; but also from things most harmefull and hatefull to mankinde, such as Serpents, Snakes, and Basilisks. That so wee might clearely discerne, that these engines were made for no other purpose, nor with other intent, but onely to be imployed for the speedy and cruell slaughter of men; and that by onely hearing them named we might detest and abhorre them, as pernicious enemies of our lives. I let passe other engines of this ofspring, being for their quantitie small, but so much the more pernicious and harmefull, for that they nearer assaile our lives, and may trayterously and forthwith seaze upon us not thinking nor fearing any such thing; so that we can scarse have any meanes of escape; such are Pistolls and other small hand-guns, which for shortnesse you may carry in your pocket, and so privily and suddainly taking them forth oppresse the carelesse and secure. Fowling peices which men usually carry upon their shoulders, are of the middle ranke of these engines, as also Muskets

The danger of Pistolls.

and Caleevers, which you cannot well discharge unlesse lying upon a Rest, which therefore may be called Breast-guns for that they are not laid to the cheeke, but against the Breast by reason of their weight and shortnesse; All which have been invented for the commodity of footemen, and light horsemen. This middle sort of engine we call in Latine by a generall name *Sclopus*, in imitation of the sound, and the Italians who terme it *Sclopetere*; the French call it *Harquebuse*, a word likewise borrowed from the Italians, by reason of the touch-hole by which you give fire to the peice, for the Italians call a hole *Buzio*. It is tearmed, *Arcus i.e.* a Bow, for that at this present it holds the same place in martiall affaires, as the Bow did of old; and as the Archers formerly, so at this day the Musquetiers are placed in front. From the same wretched shoppe and magazine of cruelty, are all sorts of Mines, Countermines, pots of fire, traines, fiery Arrowes, Lances, Crossebowes, barrells, balls of fire, burning faggots, Granats, and all such fiery engines and Inventions, which closely stuffed with fewell and matter for fire, and cast by the defendants upon the bodies and Tents of the assailants, easily take fire by the violence of their motion. Certainely a most miserable and pernicious kinde of invention, whereby we often see a thousand of heedelesse men blowne up with a mine by the force of gunpouder; otherwhiles in the very heate of the conflict you may see the stoutest souldiers seazed upon with some of these fiery Engines, to burne in their harnesse, no waters being sufficiently powerfull to restraine and quench the raging and wasting violence of such fire cruelly spreading over the body and bowells. So it was not sufficient to have armes, Iron and fire to mans destruction, unlesse also that the stroake might be more speedy, we had furnished them, as it were with wings, so to fly more hastily to our owne perdition, furnishing sithe-bearing death with wings so more speedily to oppresse man, for whose preservation, all things conteined in the world were created by God. Verily when I consider with my selfe all the sorts of warlike

A comparison of the ancient weapons with the moderne.

Engines, which the ancients used, whether in the field in set battells, as Bowes, Darts, Crossebowes, Slings; or in the assault of Citties, and shaking or overturning their walls, as Rammes, Horses, woodden towres, slings and such like; they seeme to me certaine childish sports and games made onely in imitation of the former. For these moderne inventions are such as easily exceede all the best appointed and cruell Engines which can bee mentioned or thought upon, in the shape, cruelty and appearance of their operations. For what in the world is thought more horrid or fearefull than thunder and lightning? and yet the hurtfulnesse of thunder is almost nothing to the cruelty of these infernall Engines; which may easily appeare by comparing together *Plin. Lib. 2.* both their effects. Man alone of all creatures is not alwayes *Cap.* 54. killed by being touched with thunder; but it immediatly killeth all other things which are subject to bee toucht therewith.

Nature bestowing this honour upon him, seeing so many creatures exceede him in strength: For all things ly contrary to man; and man, unlesse hee bee overthrowne with it, doth not dye thereof. But these fire-spitting Engines doe no more spare man, than they doe other creatures, and kill without difference from whence soever they come, whither soever they are carried, and howsoever they touch. There are many, but more are said to be the remedies against *Plin. Lib. 2.* thunder; for beside the charmes whereby the ancient *Cap.* 55. Romans did suppose they might be driven away, they never penetrate deeper into ground than five foote, therefore such as were fearefull thought the deeper Caves most safe. Of those things which grow out of the earth they doe not touch the Bay tree, and that was the cause that it was counted a signe of victory both in ancient and moderne *Sueton. in* times. Wherefore *Tiberius Cæsar* otherwise a contemner of *Tiberio.* God and religion, as hee who indued with the Mathematicall sciences thought all things governed by fate, yet because hee exceedingly feared thunder, hee alwayes carried a Lawrell wreath about his necke when the aire was troubled, for that this kind of leafe is reported not to be touched by thunder. Some report that he made him tents of Seales skinnes, because it toucheth not this kinde of creature of all these things that live in the Sea, as neither the Eagle amongst birds, which for that is fained to be *Joves* squire. But on the contrary, charmes, the victorious Bay, the Seale or Sea-calfe, the Eagle or any such thing profits nothing against the violence of these fiery Engines: no not a wall of tenne foote thicke will advantage. Lastly, this argues the immense violence of brasen Cannons above thunder, for that thunder may be dispersed and driven away with the noyse and ringing of Bells, the sounding of Trumpets, the tinkling of brasen kettles, yea also by the shooting of such great Ordinance; to wit, the clouds, by whose collision and fight the Thunder is caused, being dispersed by this violent agitation of the ayre, or else driven further to more remote parts of the skies. But their fury once provoked, is stayed by no opposition, appeased by no remedy. As there are certaine seasons of the yeare, so also there are certaine Regions of the earth, wherein Thunder is seldome or never heard. Thunders are rare in Winter and Summer, and that for contrary causes; for that in Winter the dense aire is thickned with a thicker coate of clouds, and the frosty and cold exhalation of the earth extinguisheth what fiery vapours soever it receives; which thing keepes *Scythia* and the cold countries about it free from Thunder. And on the contrary, too much heate preserves Egypt. For hot and dry exhalations of the earth are condensed into very thinne, subtile and weake clouds. But as the invention, so also the harme and tempest of great Ordinance, like a contagious pestilence is spread and rages over all the earth, and the skies at all times sound againe with their reports. The Thunder and Lightning commonly gives but one blow, or stroke, and that commonly strikes but one man of a multitude; But one great Cannon at one shot may spoyle and kill an hundred men. Thunder, as a thing naturall falls by chance, one while upon an high oake, another while upon the top

The wondrous force of great Ordinance.

Plin. Lib. 2: Cap. 50.

of a mountaine, and somewhiles on some lofty towre, but seldome upon man. But this hellish Engine tempered by the malice and guidance of man, assailes man onely, and takes him for his onely marke, and directs his bullets against him. The Thunder by its noyse as a messenger sent before, foretells the storme at hand; but, which is the chiefe mischiefe, this infernall Engine roares as it strikes, and strikes as it roares, sending at one and the same time the deadly bullet into the breast, and the horrible noyse into the eare. Wherefore we all of us rightfully curse the author of so pernicious an Engine; on the contrary praise those to the skies, who endeavour by words and pious exhortations to dehort Kings from their use, or else labour by writing and operation to apply fit medicines to wounds made by these Engines. Which hath moved me, that I have written hereof almost with the first of the French. But before I shall doe this, it seemeth not amisse, so to facilitate the way to the treatise I intend to write of wounds made by Gunshot, to premise two Discourses, by which I may confute and take away certaine erronious opinions which have possessed the mindes of divers; for that unlesse these be taken away, the essence and nature of the whole disease cannot be understood, nor a fitting remedy applyed by him which is ignorant of the disease.

The arguments of the following discourses.   The first Discourse which is dedicated to the Reader, repells and condemnes by reasons and examples the method of curing prescribed by *John de Vigo*,[1] whereby he cauterizes the wounds made by Gunshot, supposing them venenate; and on the contrary proves that order of curing which is performed by suppuratives, to be so salutary and gentle, as that prescribed by *Vigo* is full of errour and cruelty.

The second[2] dedicated to the King, teaches that the same wounds, are of themselves voyd of all poison, and therefore that all their malignity depends upon the fault of the aire, and ill humours predominant in the bodies of the patients.

---

[1] *Practica in Arte Chirurgica Copiosa*, Rome, 1514.
[2] Not included here.

The First Discourse
WHEREIN WOUNDS MADE BY GUNSHOT
ARE FREED FROM BEING BURNT OR
CAUTERIZED ACCORDING TO *Vigoes* METHODE

IN the yeare of our Lord 1536. *Francis* the French King, for his acts in warre and peace stiled the Great, sent a puissant Army beyond the Alpes, under the governement and leading of *Annas* of Mommorancie[1] high Constable of France, both that he might releeve *Turin* with victualls, souldiers, and all things needefull, as also to recover the Citties of that Province taken by the Marquis of *Guast* Generall of the Emperours forces. I was in the Kings Army the Chirurgion of Monsieur of *Montejan* Generall of the foote. The Imperialists had taken the straits of *Suze*, the Castle of *Villane*, and all the other passages; so that the Kings army was not able to drive them from their fortifications but by fight. In this conflict there were many wounded on both sides with all sorts of weapons, but cheefely with bullets. I will tell the truth, I was not very expert at that time in matters of Chirurgery; neither was I used to dresse wounds made by Gunshot. Now I had read in *John de Vigo* that wounds made by Gunshot were venenate or poisoned, and that by reason of the Gunpouder; Wherefore for their cure, it was expedient to burne or cauterize them with oyle of Elders scalding hot, with a little Treacle[2] mixed therewith. But for that I gave no great credite neither to the author, nor remedy, because I knew that caustickes could not be powred into wounds, without excessive paine; I, before I would runne a hazard, determined to see whether the Chirurgions, who went with me in the army, used any other manner of dressing to these wounds. I observed and saw that all of them used that Method of dressing which *Vigo* prescribes; and that they filled as full

Lib. 1. *de Vulner. Cap.* 8.

[1] Anne, first Duke of Montmorency, 1492–156
[2] Treacle, i.e. theriacs, or antidotes to poison.

as they could, the wounds made by Gunshot with Tents and pledgets dipped in this scalding Oyle, at the first dressings; which encouraged me to doe the like to those, who came to be dressed of me. It chanced on a time, that by reason of the multitude that were hurt, I wanted this Oyle. Now because there were some few left to be dressed, I was forced, that I might seeme to want nothing, and that I might not leave them undrest, to apply a digestive made of the yolke of an egge, oyle of Roses, and Turpentine. I could not sleepe all that night, for I was troubled in minde, and the dressing of the precedent day, (which I judged unfit) troubled my thoughts; and I feared that the next day I should finde them dead, or at the point of death by the poyson of the wound, whom I had not dressed with the scalding oyle. Therefore I rose early in the morning, I visited my patients, and beyound expectation, I found such as I had dressed with a digestive onely, free from vehemencie of paine to have had good rest, and that their wounds were not inflamed, nor tumifyed; but on the contrary the others that were burnt with the scalding oyle were feaverish, tormented with much paine, and the parts about their wounds were swolne. When I had many times tryed this in divers others, I thought thus much, that neither I nor any other should ever cauterize any wounded with Gun-shot. When wee first came to *Turin*, there was there a Chirurgion farre more famous than all the rest in artificially and happily curing wounds made by Gun-shot; wherefore I laboured with all diligence for two yeeres time to gaine his favour and love, that so at the length, I might learne of him, what kinde of Medicine that was, which he honoured with the glorious title of Balsame, which was so highly esteemed by him, and so happy and successfull to his patients; yet could I not obtaine it. It fell out a small while after that the Marshall of *Montejan* the Kings Lieftenant, Generall there in *Piemont* dyed, wherefore I went unto my Chirurgion, and told him that I could take no pleasure in living there, the favourer and *Macenas* of my

What chance may doe in finding out of remedies.

studies being taken away; and that I intended forthwith to returne to *Paris*, and that it would neither hinder, nor discredit him to teach his remedy to me, who should be so farre remote from him. When he heard this, he made no delay, but presently wished mee to provide two Whelpes, 1 pound of earth-wormes, 2 pounds of oyle of Lillyes, sixe ounces of Venice Turpentine, and one ounce of *Aqua vitæ*. In my presence he boyled the Whelpes put alive into that oyle, untill the flesh came from the bones, then presently he put in the Wormes, which he had first killed in white wine, that they might so be clensed from the earthy drosse wherewith they are usually repleate, and then hee boyled them in the same oyle so long, till they became dry, and had spent all their juyce therein: then hee strayned it through a towell without much pressing; and added the Turpentine to it, and lastly the *aqua vitæ*. Calling God to witnesse, that he had no other Balsame, wherewith to cure wounds made with Gunshot, and bring them to suppuration. Thus he sent me away as rewarded with a most pretious gift, requesting me to keepe it as a great secret, and not to reveale it to any.

The description of oyle of Whelpes.

When I came to *Paris*, I went to visite *Silvius*[1] the Kings professor of Physicke well knowne by name to all schollers for his great learning; he kept me long that so I might dine with him, and diligently enquires of me, if I had observed any new Method of curing wounds made by Gun-shot, and combustions occasioned by Gunpowder. Then I affirmed to him that Gun-pouder did not participate any thing of poyson, for that none of these things, whereof it is compounded are poysonous; which reason ought to free the whole composition from suspicion of poyson. And that experience confirmed this reason, for I had seene many soldiers, who would drinke a great quantity of this powder with wine, because they were perswaded, that this drinke would free them from maligne symptomes when they were wounded, yet I give no credit to this perswasion; and

Gun-pouder not poisonous.

---

[1] Sylvius, or Jacques Dubois.

lastly for that many without any harme, strew this pouder upon rebellious ulcers. For the Bullets, I affirme, that they cannot conceive such heate, as to become causticke. For if

Bullets shot out of a Gun doe not burne.

you shoot them out of a Gun against a hard stone, yet you may presently take them up without any harme in your hands, though by striking upon the stone, they should become more hot. For the combustions caused by Gunpouder, I observed no speciall nor peculiar remedy, which might make their cure different from other combustions. To which purpose I related this ensuing history.

A Historie:

One of the Marshall of *Montejan* his Kitchin boyes, fell by chance into a Caldron of Oyle being even almost boyling hot; I being called to dresse him, went to the next Apothecaries to fetch refrigerating medicines commonly used in this case: there was present by chance a certaine old countrey woman, who hearing that I desired medicines for a burne, perswaded mee at the first dressing, that I should lay to raw Onions beaten with a little salt; for so I should hinder the breaking out of blisters or pustules, as shee had

A medicine hindering blistring in burnes, or scalds.

found by certaine and frequent experience. Wherefore I thought good to try the force of her Medicine upon this greasy scullion. I the next day found those places of his body whereto the Onions lay, to bee free from blisters, but the other parts which they had not touched, to be all blistered.

A Historie.

It fell out a while after, that a German of *Montejan* his guard had his flasque full of Gunpouder set on fire, whereby his hands and face were grievously burnt: I being called, laid the Onions beaten as I formerly told you, to the middle of his face, and to the rest I laid medicines usually applyed to burnes. At the second dressing I observed the part dressed with the Onions quite free from blisters and excoriation, the other being troubled with both; whereby I gave credit to the Medicine. Besides also, I lastly told him this, that I had observed, that that was the readiest to draw forth bullets shot into the body, which sets the patients in the same posture and site, as hee was when hee received his hurt. Which things when I had told him, together with many other handled at large in this worke, the good old man requested mee to publish in print my opinions concerning these things, that so the erronious and hurtfull opinion of *Vigo* might bee taken out of mens minds. To whose earnest entreaty when I had assented, I first of all caused to be drawne and carved many Instruments fit to draw forth Bullets and other strange bodies; then a short while after I first published this worke in the yeare of our Lord 1545. which when I found to bee well liked and approved by many, I thought good to set it forth the second time somewhat amended in the yeare 1552. And the third time augmented in many particulars in the yeare 1564. For I having followed many warres, and deteined as Chirurgion in beseiged Citties, as *Metz* and *Hesdin*, had observed many things under five Kings, whom I served with diligence and content. I had learnt many things from most expert Chirurgions, but more from all learned Physitions, whose familiarity and favour for that purpose I always laboured to acquire with all diligence and honest Arts; that so I might become more learned and skillfull by their familiarity and discourse, if there was any thing especially in this matter and kind of wounds, which was hid from me, or whereof I was not well assured. Of which number I have knowne very few, who any thing seene in this kind of operation eyther by study, or experience in Warres, who have not thought that wounds made by Gunshot ought to be dressed at the first with suppurative medicines, and not with scalding and Causticke Oyle.

Wounds made by Gunshot must be dressed with suppuratives.

For this I affirme, which then also I testified to this good man, that I have found very many wounds made in the fleshy parts by Gunshot, as easily cured as other wounds, which bee made by contusing things. But in the parts of the body where the bullet meets with bones and nervous particles, both because it teares and rends into small peeces those things which resist, not onely where it touches, but

The causes of difficultie in this cure.

further also, through the violence of the blow, therefore it causeth many and greevous symptomes, which are stubborne and difficult, and oft times impossible to cure, especially in bodies replete with ill humors, in an ill constitution of the heaven and ayre, such as is hot, moyst and foggy weather, which therefore is subject to putrifaction; and in like manner a freezing and cold season, which uses to mortifie the wounded parts not onely of those that are hurt with Bullets, but in like sort with any other weapon; nor onely in bony and nervous particles, but also in musculous. Whereby you may understand, that the difficulty of curing proceeds not from the venenate quality of the wounds, nor the combustion made by the Gunpouder, but the foulenesse of the patients bodies, and the unseasonablenesse of the aire.

A Historie.   For proofe whereof, I will set downe, that which I not long agone observed in a Scottish Nobleman the Earle of *Gordon*, Lord of *Achindon*, whom I cured at the appointment of the Queene Mother. He was shot through both his thighes with a Pistoll, the bone being not hurt nor touched; and yet the 32. day after the wound he was perfectly healed, so that hee had neither feaver nor any other symptome which came upon the wound. Whereof there are worthy witnesses, the Archbishop of *Glasco*, the Scottish Embassadour, *Francis Brigart* and *John Altine*, Doctors of Physicke, as also *James Guillemeau* the Kings Chirurgion, and *Giles Buzet* a Scottish Chirurgion, who all of them wondred that this Gentleman was so soone healed, no acride medicine being applyed. This I have thought good to recite and set downe, that the Readers may understand, that I for 30. yeares agoe had found the way to cure wounds

What makes Chirurgions sometimes use causticks in curing wounds made by Gunshot.   made by Gunshot, without scalding oyle or any other, more acrid medicine; unlesse by accident the illnesse of the patients bodies and of the aire caused any maligne symptomes, which might require such remedies besides the regular and ordinary way of curing, which shall bee more amply treated of in the following discourse.[1]

[1] Not included here.

OF MUMIA

A discourse of Mumia, *or Mummie.*

PERADVENTURE it may seeme strange what may be the cause, why in this Treatise of curing contusions, or bruises, I have made no mention of giving Mummie either in bole, or potion to such as have falne from high places, or have beene otherwise bruised, especially seeing it is so common and usuall, yea the very first and last medicine of almost all our practitioners at this day in such a case. But seeing I understood, and had learnt from learned Physitions, that in using remedies, the indication must alwaies be taken from that which is contrary to the disease, how could I? how can any other give Mummie in this kinde of disease, seeing we cannot as yet know what Mummie is, or what is the nature and essence thereof? So that it cannot certainely be judged, whether it have a certaine property contrary to the nature and effects of contusions. This how it may have, I have thought good to relate somewhat at large; neither doe the Physitions who prescribe Mummie, nor the Authours that have written of it, nor the Apothecaries that sell it, know any certainty thereof. For if you reade the more ancient, *Serapio,* and *Avicen,* or the moderne *Matthiolus* and *Thevet,* you shall finde quite different opinions. Aske the Merchants who bring it to us, aske the Apothecaries who buy it of them, to sell it to us, and you shall heare them speake diversly heereof, that in such variety of opinions, there is nothing certaine and manifest.

Mummie a frequent and usuall medicine in contusions.

The reason that the Author makes no mention thereof amongst his medicines.

The opinion of the *Arabians* concerning it.

Serapio and *Avicen* have judged Mummie to bee nothing else but *Pissasphaltum*; now *Pissasphaltum* is a certaine froth or foame rising from the Sea, or Sea waters; this same foame as long as it swimmes upon the water is soft and in some sort liquide: but being driven upon the shore by force of tempest, and working of the sea, and sticking in the cavityes of the rockes, it concreates into somewhat a harder substance than dryed pitch, as *Dioscorides* saith.

Lib. 4, *cap.*
84.

Belonius saith, that Mummie is onely knowne to *Ægypt* and *Greece*. Others write that it is mans flesh, taken from the carcases of such as are dead, and covered over in the sandes in the desartes of *Arabia*; in which Countrey they say the

Another
opinion of
Mummie.

sands are sometimes carried and raysed up with such force and violence of the windes, that they overthrow and suffocate such passingers as they meete withall; the flesh of these dryed by the sand and winde they affirme to be Mummy.

Mathiolus following the more usuall and common opinion, writes that Mummie is nothing else than a liquor flowing from the Aromaticke embalments of dead bodyes,

Another.

which becomes dry and hard. For understanding whereof you must know from all manner of antiquity, that the Egyptians have beene most studious in burying and embalming their dead; not for that end that they should become medicines for such as live, for they did not so much as respect or imagine so horride a wickednesse. But either for that they held an opinion of the generall resurrection, or that in these monuments they might have something, whereby they might keepe their dead friends in perpetuall remembrance.

Thevet not much dissenting from his owne opinion, writes that the true Mummie is taken from the monuments and stony tombes of the anciently dead in Egypt, the chinkes of which tombes were closed, and cimented with such diligence; but the enclosed bodyes embalmed with precious spices with such art for eternity, that the linnen vestures which were wrapt about them presently after their death, may be seene whole even to this day; but the bodies themselves, are so fresh that you would judge them scarce to have been three dayes buryed. And yet in those Sepulchers and Vaultes from whence these bodyes are taken, there have beene some corpes of two thousand yeeres old. The same, or their broken members are brought to Venice from Syria and Egypt, and thence disperst over all Christendom. But according to the different condition of men, the matter of their embalments were divers; for the bodyes of the Nobility or Gentry are embalmed with Myrrhe, Aloes, Saffron, and other precious spices, and Drugs; but the bodyes of the common sort whose poverty and want of meanes could not undergoe such cost, were embalmed with *asphaltum* or *pissasphaltum*.

Now *Mathiolus* saith that all the Mummie which is brought into these parts is of this last kinde and condition. For the Noble men and cheefe of the province so religiously addicted to the monuments of their ancestors, would never suffer the bodyes of their friends, and kindred to be transported hither for filthy gaine, and such detested use, as we shall shew more at large at the end of this worke.

What our Mummie usually is.

Which thing sometimes mooved certaine of our French Apothecaries, men wonderous audacious, and covetous, to steale by night the bodyes of such as were hanged, and embalming them with salt and Drugges they dryed them in an Oven, so to sell them thus adulterated in steed of true Mummie. Wherefore wee are thus compelled both foolishly and cruelly to devoure the mangled and putride particles of the carcasses of the basest people of Egypt, or of such as are hanged, as though there were no other way to helpe or recover one bruised with a fall from a high place, than to bury man by an horrid insertion in their, that is, in mans guts. Now if this Drugge were any way powerfull for that they require, they might perhaps have some pretence, for this their more than barbarous inhumanity.

But the case stands thus, that this wicked kinde of Drugge, doth nothing helpe the diseased, in that case,

Mummie is no way good for contusions,

wherefore and wherein it is administred, as I have tryed an hundred times, and as *Thevet* witnesses, he tryed in himselfe, when as he tooke some thereof by the advice of a certaine Jewish Physition in Egypt, from whence it is brought; but it also inferres many troublesome symptomes, as the paine of the heart or stomacke, vomiting and stinke of the mouth.

But hurtfull, and how?

I perswaded by these reasons, doe not onely my selfe prescribe any hereof to my patients, but also in consultations, endeavour what I may, that it bee not prescribed by others. It is farre better according to *Galens* opinion *in Method. med.* to drinke some oxycrate, which by its frigidity restraines the flowing blood, and by its tenuity of substance dissolves and discusses the congealed clotts thereof. Many reasons of learned Physitions (from whom I have learned this history of Mummie) drawne from Philosophy, whereby they make it apparent, that there can be no use of this or that Mummie in contusions, or against flowing or congealed blood, I willingly omit, for that I thinke it not much beneficiall to Chirurgions to insert them heere.

The effects of oxycrate in Contusions.

OF AMPUTATIONS

The signes of a perfect Necrosis *or Mortification.*

YOU shall certainly know that a Gangreene is turned into a Sphacell, or mortification, and that the part is wholly and throughly dead, if it looke of a blacke colour, and bee colder than stone to your touch, the cause of which coldnesse is not occasioned by the frigiditie of the aire; if there bee a great softnesse of the part, so that if you presse it with your finger it rises not againe, but retaines the print of the impression. If the skinne come from the flesh lying under it; if so great and strong a smell exhale (especially in an ulcerated Sphacell) that the standers by cannot endure or suffer it; if a sanious moisture, viscide, greene or blackish flow from thence; if it bee quite destitute of sense and motion, whether it be pulled, beaten, crushed, pricked, burnt, or cut off. Here I must admonish the young Chirurgion, that hee be not deceived concerning the losse or privation of the sense of the part.

For I know very many deceived as thus; the patients pricked on that part would say they felt much paine there. But that feeling is oft deceiptfull, as that which proceeds rather from the strong apprehension of great paine which formerly reigned in the part, than from any facultie of feeling as yet remaining. A most cleare and manifest argument of this false and deceitful sense appeares after the amputation of the member; for a long while after they will complaine of the part which is cut away. *A note concerning the unsensiblenesse of the part.*

Verily it is a thing wondrous strange and prodigious, and which will scarse be credited, unlesse by such as have seene with their eyes, and heard with their eares the patients who have many moneths after the cutting away of the Legge, grievously complained that they yet felt exceeding great paine of that Leg so cut off. Wherefore have a speciall care least this hinder your intended amputation; a thing pittifull, yet absolutely necessary for to preserve the life of the patient and all the rest of his body, by cutting away of that member which hath all the signes of a Sphacell and perfect mortification; for otherwise the neglected fire will in a moment spread over all the body, and take away all hope of remedy; for thus *Hippocrates* wisheth: That Sections, Ustions, and Terebrations must bee performed as soone as neede requires. *A wondrous symptome.* *Sect. 7. Lib. 6. Epidem.*

Where Amputation must be made.

It is not sufficient to know that Amputation is necessary; but also you must learne in what place of the dead part, it *The controversy decided.*

must bee done, and herein the wisedome and judgement of the Chirurgion is most apparent. Art bids to take hold of the quicke, and to cut off the member in the sound flesh; but the same art wisheth us, to preserve whole that which is sound, as much as in us lies. I will shew thee by a familiar example how thou maist carry thy selfe in these difficulties. Let us suppose, that the foote is mortified even to the anckle; here you must attentively marke in what place you must cut it off. For unlesse you take hold of the quicke flesh in the amputation, or if you leave any putrefaction, you profit nothing by amputation, for it will creepe and spread over the rest of the body. It befits Physicke ordained for the preservation of mankind, to defend from the iron or instrument and all manner of injurie, that which enjoyes life and health. Wherefore you shall cut off as little of that which is sound as you possibly can; yet so that you rather cut away that which is quicke, than leave behind any thing *Lib. 7. Cap.* that is perished, according to the advice of *Celsus.* Yet oft *33.* times the commodity of the action of the rest of the part, and as it were a certaine ornament thereof, changes this counsell. For if you take these two things into your consideration they will induce you in this propounded case and example, to cut off the Legge some five fingers breadth under the knee. For so the patient may more fitly use the rest of his Legge and with lesse trouble, that is, he may the better goe on a woodden Legge; for otherwise, if according to the common rules of Art, you cut it off close to that which is perished the patient will be forced with trouble to use three Legges instead of two.

An observ-   For I so knew Captaine *Francis Clerke,* when as his foote *able History.* was strucken off with an iron bullet shot forth of a man of warre, and afterwards recovered and healed up, hee was much troubled and wearied with the heavy and unprofitable burden of the rest of his Legge, wherefore though whole and sound he caused the rest thereof to bee cut off, some five fingers breadth below his knee; and verily hee useth it with much more ease and facility than before in performance of any motion. Wee must doe otherwise if any such thing happen in the Arme; that is, you must cut off as little of the sound part as you can. For the actions of the Legges much differ from these of the armes, and chiefly in this that the body rests not, neither is carried upon the armes, as it is upon the feete and Legges.

How the section or amputation must be performed.

The first care must be of the patients strength, wherefore let him be nourished with meats of good nutriment, easie digestion, and such as generate many spirits; as with the yolkes of Egges, and bread tosted and dipped in Sacke or Muskedine. Then let him bee placed, as is fit, and drawing the muscles upwards toward the sound parts, let them be tyed with a straite ligature a little above that place of the member which is to be cut off, with a strong and broad fillet like that which women usually bind up their haire withall; This ligature hath a threefold use; the first is, that it hold the muscles drawne up together with the skin, so that retiring backe presently after the performance of the worke, they may cover the ends of the cut bones, and serve them in stead of boulsters or pillowes when they are healed up, and so suffer with lesse paine the compression in susteining the rest of the body; besides also by this meanes the wounds are the sooner healed and cicatrized; for by how much more flesh or skinne is left upon the ends of the bones, by so much they are the sooner healed and cicatrized. The second is, for that it prohibites the fluxe of blood by pressing and shutting up the veines and arteries. The third is, for that it much dulls the sense of the part by stupefying it; the animall spirits by the straite compression being hindred from passing in by the Nerves: Wherefore when you have made your ligature, cut the flesh even to the bone with a sharpe and well cutting incision knife, or with a crooked knife, such as is here expressed.

The Ligature of the part.

Now you must note, that there usually lyes betweene the bones, a portion of certaine muscles, which you cannot

A caution to be observed.

easily cut with a large incision or dismembring knife;
wherefore you must carefully divide it and separate it
wholly from the bone, with an instrument made neatly
like a crooked incision knife. I thought good to advertise
thee hereof; for if thou shouldest leave any thing besides
the bone to bee divided by the saw, you would put the
patient to excessive paine in the performance thereof; for

A crooked knife fit for dismembring; or a dismembring knife.

The Figure of such a Saw.

soft things as flesh tendons and membranes, cannot be easily
cut with a saw. Therefore when you shall come to the
bared bone, all the other parts being wholly cut asunder
and divided, you shall nimbly divide it with a little saw
about some foote and three inches long, and that as neare
to the sound flesh as you can. And then you must smooth
the front of the bone which the saw hath made rough.

How to stanch the bleeding when the member is taken off.

When you have cut off and taken away the member, let
it bleed a little according to the strength of the patient, that
so the rest of the part may afterwards be lesse obnoxious
to inflammation and other symptomes; Then let the Veines
and Arteries be bound up as speedily and streightly as you
can; that so the course of the flowing blood may bee

stopped and wholly stayed. Which may be done by taking
hold of the vessells with your Crowes beake, whereof this
is the figure.

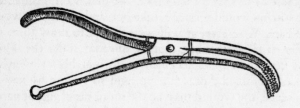

*The Crowes beake fit for to draw the vessells forth of the flesh wherein
they lye hid, that so they may be tyed or bound fast.*

The ends of the vessells lying hid in the flesh, must be taken
hold of & drawn with this instrument forth of the muscles
whereinto they presently after the amputation withdrew
themselves, as all parts are still used to withdraw themselves towards their originalls. In performance of this
worke, you neede take no great care, if you together with
the vessells comprehend some portion of the neighbouring
parts, as of the flesh, for hereof will ensue no harme; but
the vessells will so bee consolidated with the more ease,
than if they being bloodlesse parts should grow together
by themselves. To conclude, when you have so drawne
them forth, binde them with a strong double thred.

How to draw forth the vessells and binde them.

How after the blood is stanched, you must dresse the wounded member.

When you have tyed the Vessells, loose your Ligature
which you made above the place of amputation; then draw
together the lippes of the wound with foure stitches made
acrosse, having taken good hold of the flesh; for thus you
shall draw over the bones that part of the skinne and cut
muscles drawne upwards before the amputation, and cover
them as close as you can, that so the ayre may the lesse
come at them, and that so the wound may bee the more

How the lips of the dis-membred part are to be joyned together.

speedily agglutinated. But when wee say, draw together the lippes of the wound with foure stitches, you must not so understand it, as that you must endeavour, to draw them so close as to touch each other, for that is impossible; for the stitches would sooner breake out, and so the part would lye bare. Wherefore it will be sufficient to draw them indifferent close together, that so you may suffer the skinne and flesh thereunder to enjoy its former liberty which it possest before the drawing up, and so in fine by natures assistance, the wound may be the more easily agglutinated.

How you must stoppe the bleeding, if any of the bound up vessels chance to get loose.

The businesse hitherto being performed as we said, if peradventure it happen that any bandage of any of the vessels be unloosed; then must you againe binde the member with that kinde of Ligature which you did before the amputation thereof. Or else, which is better, more easily and lesse painefull, let your servant taking hold of the member with both his hands, pressing his fingers strait, stoppe the passage of the loosed vessell, for so hee may stanch the bleeding. Then let the worke-master take a needle some foure fingers long, square, and having sharpe edges, drawing after it a three or foure doubled strong thred. With this let him binde the vessell after the following manner. Let him thrust his needle on the outside into the flesh, some halfe fingers breadth from the loosed vessell untill he come to the end thereof, then let him put it about it, and bring it backe againe, but so that there be no more than the space of a fingers bredth betweene the going in, and comming forth of the needle. In this space let him put a linnen ragge three or foure times doubled, and thereupon bind somewhat straite the two ends of the thred together. For so he shall hinder the knot from hurting the flesh which lyes under it in the bindings, and also adde strength thereto. For so the bound up orifice of the vessell will in short space be agglutinated to the adjoyning flesh, and that so firmely,

The Heamorrhagie of small vessels is not to be regarded.

that there hath never beene seene, any one drop of blood to have flowed from a vessell so bound up. But if the blood which flowes forth proceede from any small vessell, you must not use this suture and ligature, nor make any such great matter thereof; for it will quickly be stanched by the only application of Astringents presently to be mentioned.

How to performe the residue of the cure of the amputated member.

Now must we shew what medicines are fitting to be applyed after the amputation of a member; which are Emplasticks, as these which exceedingly conduce to greene wounds. As ℞. *boli arm.* ℥ iiij. *farin. vol.* ℥ ij. *picis, resinæ, an.* ℥ ij. *pulverisentur omnia subtiliss. & simul mixtis fiat pulvis*; herewith let the wound bee strewed, and lay thereupon dry Lint; but let the following repercussive or defensitive be applyed to the member.

An emplastick medicine.

℞. *Album ovorum* vj. *boli arm. sang. drac. gypsi, terræ sigill. aloës, mastiches, gallar. combust. an.* ℥ ij. *in pollinem redigantur omnia, & bene agitentur, addendo olei rosarum & myrtil. an.* ℥ j. *fiat defensitivum ad formam mellis.* This ointment must bee applyed upon stoopes dipped in Oxycrate, and that so that it may not onely cover the cut member, but also be spread further and cover the neighbouring parts; as when the Legge is cut off, it must bee laid upon the joynt, and spread higher than the knee, some foure fingers upon the thigh; for it hath not onely a repercussive facultie, but it also strengthens the part, hinders defluxion by tempering the blood, aswaging paine, and hindring inflammation. It will also be good to moisten your double clothes and bandages in Oxycrate; then must you place the member in an indifferent posture upon a pillow stuffed with oaten huskes or chaffe, Stagges haire, or wheate branne. It must not be stirred after the first dressing (unlesse great necessity urge) for foure dayes in winter, but somewhat sooner in summer. For the ligatures wherewith the vessells are bound,

A repercussive.

How to place the member and how often to dresse it.

they must not be loosed, or otherwise taken away, before
the mouthes of the vessells are covered with their glue or
flesh, lest by too much haste you cause a new flux of blood.
This agglutination will be performed by applying refrigerating, astringent, and emplasticke medicines, such as this
following powder.

An emplas-
stick pouder.

℞. *boli arm. farin. hord. picis res. gypsi, an.* ℥iiij. *Aloës,*
nucum cup. cort. granat. an. ℥j. *incorporentur omnia simul, fiat*
pulvis subtilis: herewith let the whole ulcer be strewed over
for three or foure dayes space; which being ended, let onely
the seates of the vessells be poudred therewith, and that for
eight or ten dayes, so that wee neede no further doubt of
the agglutination of the vessells. In the meane space let the
digestive be applyed to the rest of the Ulcer untill it bee
come to suppuration; for then you shall give over your
digestive, and betake you to detersive and mundificative
medicines: As

Detersives.

℞. *terebinth. ven. lotæ in aqua vitæ* ℥vj. *mellis ros. colati*
℥iiij. *succi plantag. Apij, centaur. minoris, an.* ℥ij. *bulliant*
omnia simul usque ad consumptionem succorum: auferantur
ab igne, addendo farinæ fab. & hord. an. ℥j. *theriac. Gal.* ℥ss.
aloes, myrrhæ, aristoloch. an. ℥iiij. *croci* ℈j. *fiat mundificativum.*

Why after
dismem-
bring the
patients com-
plaine of
paine as if
the part were
yet remain-
ing on.

But seeing the case stands so that the Patients imagine
they have their members yet entire, and yet doe complaine
thereof (which I imagine to come to passe, for that, the cut
nerves retire themselves towards their originall, and thereby cause a paine like to convulsions; for as *Galen* writes in
his booke, *De motu musculorum,* That contraction is the true
and proper action of a nerve and muscle: and againe, extension is not so much an action as a motion:) now wee must
indeavour to give remedy to this symptome. Which may
be done by annointing the spine of the backe and all the
affected part with the following Liniment, which is very
powerfull against Convulsions, the Palsie, numnesse, and
all cold affects of the nervous bodies.

An ointment
for the spine
of the backe
against all
affects of the
nerves.

℞. *salviæ, chamæpytheos, majorana, rorismar. menth. rutæ,*
lavendulæ, an. m. j. flor. chamæmel. melilot. summit. aneth. &

hyperici, an. p. ij. baccarum lauri & juniperi an. ℥ij. radicis
pyrethri ℥ij. mastic. assæ odorat. an. ℥iss, terebinth, venet lb. j.
olei lumbr. aneth. catell. an. ℥vj. olei terebinth. ℥iiij. axung.
hum. ℥ij. croci ℥j. vini albi odoriferi lib. j. ceræ quantum sufficit,
contundenda contundantur pulverisanda pulverisentur, deinde
macerentur omnia in vino per noctem, postea coquantur cum oleis &
axungia prædictis in vase duplici, fiat linimentum secundum artem,
in fine adde aquæ vitæ ℥ iiij. Besides, in dressing these wounds, the Chirurgion must use diligence to procure the falling away of the ends or scalls of the bones, which the saw and the appulse of the aire never before comming hereto, have tainted; which may be done by applying to their ends actuall cauteries, that is, hot irons, in using of which you must have a speciall care that you touch not the sensible parts with fire; neither must the bones themselves bee forcibly pluckt off, but gently mooved by little and little, so that you shall thinke you and the patient have exceedingly well performed your parts if they fall away at the thirtyeth day after the Amputation. All these things being performed, you shall hinder the growth of proud flesh with the cathæreticks, such as are burnt vitrioll, the pouder of Mercurie, and other things, amongst which is Alome burnt and poudered, which is excellent in these kind of wounds whether by its selfe or mixed with others. You shall use these and such like, even unto the perfect agglutination and cicatrization of the wound, and you may of your selfe devise other things, such as these, as occasion shall offer its selfe.

How to procure the falling away of the ends of the bones.

Cathæreticks.

What just occasion moved the Author to devise this new forme
of remedy, to stanch the blood after the amputation of a
member; and to forsake the common way used almost
by all Chirurgions; which is, by application of
actuall cauteries.

Verily I confesse, I formerly have used to stanch the bleeding of members after amputation, after another manner than that I have a little before mentioned. Whereof

I am ashamed, and agreived; But what should I doe? I had observed my maisters whose method I intended to follow, alwaies to doe the like; who thought themselves singularly well appointed to stanch a flux of blood, when they were furnished with various store of hot Irons and causticke medicines, which they would use to the dismembred part, now one, then another, as they themselves thought meete. Which thing cannot be spoken, or but thought upon without great horror, much lesse acted. For this kinde of remedy could not but bring great and tormenting paine to the patient, seeing such fresh wounds made in the quicke and sound flesh are endewed with exquisite sense. Neither can any causticke be applyed to nervous bodies, but that this horrid impression of the fire will be presently communicated to the inward parts, whence horrid symptomes ensue, and oft times death it selfe. And verily of such as were burnt, the third part scarse ever recovered, and that with much adoe, for that combust wounds difficultly come to cicatrization; for by this burning are caused cruell paines, whence a Feaver, Convulsion, and oft times other accidents worse than these. Adde hereunto, that when the eschar fell away, oft times a new hæmorrhagye ensued, for stanching whereof they were forced to use other causticke and burning Instruments. Neither did these good men know any other course; so by this repetition there was great losse and waste made of the fleshy and nervous substance of the part. Through which occasion the bones were laid bare, whence many were out of hope of cicatrization, being forced for the remainder of their wretched life to carry about an ulcer upon that part which was dismembred; which also tooke away the oportunitie of fitting or putting too of an artificiall legge or arme in stead of that which was taken off.

Wherefore I must earnestly entreate all Chirurgions, that leaving this old, and too cruell way of healing, they would embrace this new, which I thinke was taught mee by the speciall favour of the sacred Deitie; for I learnt it not of my maisters, nor of any other, neither have I at any

Hot Irons not to be used.

time found it used by any. Onely I have read in *Galen*, Lib. 5. Meth.
that there was no speedier remedy for stanching of blood,
than to bind the vessels through which it flowed towards
their rootes, to wit, the Liver and Heart.

This precept of *Galen*, of binding and sowing the Veines
and Arteries in the new wounds, when as I thought it
might be drawne to these which are made by the amputation of members, I attempted it in many; yet so that at
first in my budding practise thereof, I alwayes had my
cauteries and hot Irons in a readinesse, that if any thing
happened otherwise than I expected in this my new worke,
I might fetch succour from the ancient practice, untill at
length confirmed by the happy experience of almost an
infinite number of particulars, I bid eternally adieu, to all
hot Irons and cauteries which were commonly used in this
worke. And I thinke it fit that Chirurgions doe the like.
For antiquity and custome in such things as are performed
by Art, ought not to have any sway, authority or place
contrary to reason, as they oft times have in civill affaires;
wherefore let no man say unto us, that the Ancients have
alway done thus.

The practice of the former precepts is declared, together with a
memorable history of a certaine soldier, whose arme
was taken off at the Elbow.

I thinke it fit to confirme by an example the prescribed
method of curing a Gangreene and Mortification. Whilest   A History:
I was Chirurgion to the Marshall of *Montejan* at *Turin*, a
certaine common souldier received a wound on his wrest
with a musket bullet, by which the bones and tendons
being much broken, and the nervous bodyes cruelly torne,
there followed a Gangreen, & at length a mortification
even to the Elbow; besides also an inflammation seazed
upon the middle part of his Chest, and there was as it were
a certaine disposition to a Gangreene, whereby it followed
that he was painefully and dangerously troubled with
belchings, hickettings, watchings, unquietnesse and frequent

swoundings, which occasioned many Chirurgions to
leave him as desperate. But it so fell out, that I, orecome
by his friends intreaty, undertooke the cure of this wretched
person, destitute of all humane helpe. Wherefore knowing
the mortification by its signes, I cut off the arme by the
elbow as speedily as I could, making first the ligature,
whereof I made mention; I say I tooke it off not with a
saw, but onely with an incision knife, cutting in sunder the
ligaments which held the bones together, because the sphacell was not passed the joynt of the Elbow. Neither ought
this section to be accounted strange, which is made in a
joynt; for *Hippocrates* much commends it, and saith that it
is easily healed, and that there is nothing to be feared therein besides swounding, by reason of the paine caused by
cutting the common tendons and ligaments. But such incision being made, the former Ligature could not hinder, but
much blood must flow from thence, by reason of the large
vessels that run that way. Wherefore I let the blood to flow
plentifully so to disburden the part, and so afterwards to
free it from the danger and feare of inflammation and a
Gangreene; then presently I stanched the blood with an hot
Iron, for as yet I knew no other course. Then gently loosing
the Ligature I scarified that part of the brawn of the Arme
which was Gangreenated, with many and deepe incisions,
shunning and not touching the inner part, by reason of the
multitude of the large vessels and Nerves which runne that
way; then I presently applyed a cautery to some of the
incisions, both to stanch the bleeding, and draw forth the
virulent *sanies* which remained in the part. And then I
assailed and overcame the spreading putrefaction by putting and applying the formerly prescribed medicines; I used
all sorts of restrictive medicines, to stay the inflammation
of the Chest; I also applyed Epithema's to the region of
the heart, and gave him cordiall potions and boles, neither
did I desist from using them untill such time as his belching,
hicketting and swoundings had left him. Whilest I more
attentively intended these things, another mischeife assailes

Dismem-
bring at a
joynt.

Sect. 4. *lib.
de Art.*

my patient, to wit, Convulsions, and that not through any
fault of him or me, but by the naughtinesse of the place
wherein hee lay, which was in a Barne every where full of
chinkes and open on every side, and then also it was in the
midst of winter raging with frost and snow and all sorts of
cold; neyther had he any fire or other thing necessary for
preservation of life, to lessen these injuries of the Aire and
place; Now his joints were contracted, his teeth set, and his
mouth and face were drawne awry, when as I pittying his
case made him to bee carried into the neighbouring Stable
which smoaked with much horse dung, and bringing in
fire in two chafendishes, I presently annointed his necke
and all the spine of his backe, shunning the parts of the
Chest, with liniments formerly described for convulsions;
then straight way I wrapped him in a warme linnen cloth,
and buried him even to the necke in hot dung, putting a
little fresh straw about him; when hee had stayed there
some three dayes, having at length a gentle scowring or
flux of his belly, and plentifull sweate, hee begun by little
and little to open his mouth and teeth which before were
set and close shut. Having got by this meanes some oppor-
tunitie better to doe my businesse, I opened his mouth as
much as I pleased, by putting this following Instrument
betweene his Teeth:

Burying in hot horse dung helpes Convulsions.

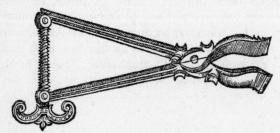

*A Dilater made for to open the mouth and Teeth by the meanes of a
screw in the end thereof.*

Now drawing out the Instrument I kept his mouth open
by putting in a willow sticke on each side thereof, that so

I might the more easily feede him with meats soone made, as with Cowes milke and reare eggs, untill hee had recovered power to eate, the convulsion having left him. Hee by this meanes freed from the Convulsion, I then againe begun the cure of his arme, and with an actuall cautery seare the end of the bone, so to dry up the perpetuall effluxe of corrupt matter.

It is not altogether unworthy of your knowledge, that hee said, how that hee was wondrously delighted by the application of such actuall cauteries, a certaine tickling running the whole length of the arme by reason of the gentle diffusion of the heate by applying the causticke; which same thing I have observed in many others; especially in such as lay upon the like occasion in the Hospitall of *Paris*. After this cauterizing there fell away many and large scalles of the bone, the freer appulse of the aire than was fit making much thereto; besides when there was place for fomentation, with the decoction of red Rose leaves, Wormewood, Sage, Bay leaves, flowers of Chamomile, Melilote, Dill, I so comforted the part that I also at the same time by the same meanes drew and tooke away the virulent *Sanies*, which firmely adhered to the flesh and bones.

Lastly, it came to passe, that by Gods assistance, these meanes I used, and my carefull diligence, he at length recovered. Wherefore I would admonish the young Chirurgion, that hee never account any so desperate, as to give him for lost, content to have let him goe with prognosticks; for as an ancient Doctor writes; That as in Nature, so in diseases there are also Monsters.

A fomentation for a Convulsion.

Monsters or miracles in diseases.

OF FRACTURES

What a Fracture is, and what the differences thereof are.

A FRACTURE, in Galens opinion, is the solution of *Lib. 6. method.* continuitie in a bone, which by the Greeks is called *Catagma*. There are many sorts of hurting or offending the bones: as the drawing them asunder, luxation, or putting them out of joynt; their unnaturall growing together, their cutting or dividing a-sunder; contusion, abscesse, putrefaction, rottennesse, the *periostium* being laid bare, violated or lost; and lastly, that whereof we now treate, a Fracture. Again, the varieties of Fractures are almost infinite. For one is complete and perfect, another imperfect; one runnes long-wise, another transverse, another oblique; one while it is broken into great peeces, another while into little and small scales, which have eyther a blunt, or else a sharpe end, and pricke the adjacent bodies of the muscles, nerves, veines or arteries. It somtimes happens, that the bone is not broken into *What it is for a bone to be broken Raphanedon.* splinters, that is, long-wayes, but together, and at once into two peeces overthwart, which Fracture is called *Raphanedon*, that is, after the maner of a Raddish.

A Fracture is made *Caryedon*, or like a nut, when as the *What Caryedon; or Alphitidon.* bone flyes into many small peeces, severed each from other, as when a Nut is broken with a hammer or mallet upon an Anvile: Which fracture is also termed *Alphitidon*, by reason of the resemblance it hath to meale or floure; and such is often seene in fractures made by bullets, shot out of guns and such fiery engines. Contrary to these are those *What Schidacidon.* fractures which are called *Schidacidon*, as rent into splinters, or after the manner of a boord or peece of timber, that is, right-downe, and alongst the bone: and these fractures are eyther apparent to the eye, or else not apparent, and therefore called Capillarie, being so small, as that they cannot be perceived by the eye, unlesse you put inke upon them, and then shave them with your Scrapers. Sometimes the bone is only pressed downe by the stroke, sometimes on the contrarie it flyes up, as if it were vaulted. They call it attrition, when the bone is broken into many small fragments, and as it were scales or chips. The fragments of fractured bones are somtimes smooth and polished, otherwhiles unequall, and as it were sharpe and rough with little teeth, or prickes. Some fractures touch onely the surface of the bone, fetching off only a scale; othersome change not the site of fractured bones, but only cleaves them lengthwaies, without the plucking away of any fragment; othersome penetrate even to their marrow.

Furthermore some Fractures are simple and alone by themselves; othersome are accompanied with a troop of other affects and symptomes; as a wound, hæmorrhagye, inflammation, gangrene, and the like. Hereunto you may also adde the differences drawne from the parts which the Fractures possesse; as from the head, ribs, limbs, joynts, and other members of the bodie. Adde also these which are taken from the habit of bodies, aged, young, full of ill humors, well tempered; almost all which have their proper and peculiar indications for curing. Now the causes of Fractures, are the too violent assaults or stroaks of all externall things, which may cut, bruise, breake, or shake: in this number of causes may also be reckoned fals from high places, and infinite other things, which would be long and tedious to reckon up.

The causes of fractures.

Of the signes of a Fracture.

The first signe of a broken bone.

We may know by evident signes that a bone is broken: the first whereof, and most certaine, is, when by handling the part which we suspect to be broken, wee feele peeces

of the bone severed asunder, and heare a certaine crackling
of these peeces under our hands, caused by the attrition of
the shattered bones. Another signe is taken from the im- Another.
potencie of the part, which chiefly bewrayes its selfe, when
both the bones, the legge, and brace-bones, the ell and wand[1]
are broken. For if onely the brace-bone or wand be broken,
the Patient may goe on his legge, and stirre his arme: for
the brace-bone serves for the sustaining of the muscles, and
not of the bodie, as the legge bone doth. The third signe A third.
is drawne from the figure of the part changed besides
nature: for it is there hollow, from whence the bone is
flowne or gone, but gibbous or bunching out whither it
is runne. Great paine in the interim torments the patient
by reason of the wronged *periostium*, and that membrane
which involves the marrow and the sympathie of the adjacent parts which are compressed or pricked.

Of Prognosticks to be made in Fractures.

Wee must prognosticate in Fractures, whether they are
to end in the destruction or welfare of the patient; or
whether their cure shall be long or short, easie, or else
difficult and dangerous; and lastly, what accidents and
symptomes may happen thereupon. Hee shall easily attaine
to the knowledge of all these things, who is not onely well
seene in the anatomicall description of the bones, but also
in the temper, composition and complexion of the whole
bodie. Wherefore in the first place, I thinke good to ad- Why bones
monish the Surgeon of this, that in winter when all is stiffe are more
with cold, by a little fall, or some such sleight occasion, brittle in
frostie
the bones may be quickly and readily broken. For then the weather.
bones, being dryed by the drinesse of the ayre encompassing us, become more brittle; which everie one of the
Vulgar usually observe to happen both in waxen and tallow
candles: but when the season is moist, the bones are also
more moist, and therefore more flexible and yeelding
to the violence of the obvious and offending bodie.

[1] i.e. the ulna and radius.

Wherefore also you may gather this to the framing of your Prognosticks: That bones by reason of their naturall drinesse are not so easily agglutinated and consolidated as flesh; though in Children, according to Galen, by reason of the abundance of their humiditie, the lost substance may bee repaired, according (as they terme it) to the first intention, that is, by restoring of the same kinde of substance or matter. But in others, about the Fractures a certaine hard substance usually concreats, of that nourishment of the broken bone which abounds, which glues together the fragments thereof, being fitly put together. This substance is then termed a *Callus*, and it is so hardened in time, that the bone thereafter in the broken part is seene to be more firme and hard than it is in any other: therefore that usuall saying in Physicke is not without reason; That rest is necessarie for the uniting of broken bones. For the *Callus* is easily dissolved, if they bee moved before their perfect and solid agglutination. The matter of a *Callus* ought to be indifferent and laudible in quantitie and qualitie, even as blood which flowes for the regeneration of the lost flesh in wounds. It is fit, that there may be sufficient matter for such a *Callus*, that the part have a laudible temper, otherwise there either wil be no *Callus*, or certainly it wil grow more slowly. Fractures are far more easily repaired in yong bodies than in old: for in these there is plentie of the primigenious and radicall moisture, that is laudably holding and glutinous; and in the other there is store of watrish and excrementitious. By this you may easily conjecture, that you cannot certainely set downe a time necessarie for the generating a *Callus*: for in some it happens later, in some sooner: the cause of which varietie is also to be referred to the constitution of the yeare and region, the temper and diet of the Patient, and maner of Ligation. For, those Patients whose powers are weake, and blood watrish and thin, in these the generation of a *Callus* uses to be more slow: On the contrarie, strong powers hasten to agglutinate the bones, if there be plentie of grosse and viscous matter;

Why the solution of continuity in bones is not so easily repaired. *Gal. in arte par.*

Why bones sooner knit in yong bodies.

Meats of grosse and tough nourishment conduce to the generation of a *Callus*.

whereby it comes to passe, that meats of grosser nutriment
are to bee used, and medicines applyed which may helpe
forwards the endeavour of nature, as we shall declare hereafter. When the bones are broken neare unto the joynts,
the motion afterwards uses to be more difficult, especially
if the *Callus*, which is substituted, be somewhat thicke and
bunching forth. But if, together with the violence and force
of the Fracture, the joynts shall bee broken and bruised, the
motion will not only bee lost, but the life brought in
danger, by reason of the greatnesse of the inflammation,
which usually happens in such affects, and the excesse of
paine in a tendinous body. These fractures wherein both
the bones of the arme or legge are broken, are more difficult
to cure, than those which happen but to one of them. For
they are handled & kept in their places with more difficulty,
because that which remaines whole, serves the other for
a rest or stay to which it may leane. Moreover, there is
longer time required to substitute a *Callus* to a great bone,
than to a little one. Againe these bones which are more
rare and spongie, are sooner glued together by the interposition of a *Callus*, than these which are dense and solid.
A *Callus* sooner growes in sanguine, than in cholerick
bodies. But broken bones cannot be so happily agglutinated, nor restored in any body, but that alwaies some
asperity or unequall protuberancie may bee seene on that
part where the *Callus* is generated. Wherfore the Surgeon
ought to make artificiall Ligations, that the *Callus* may not
stand out too far, nor sinke downe too low. That Fracture
is least troublesome which is simple; on the contrarie, that is
more troublesome which is made into splinters; but that
is most troublesome and worst of all which is in small and
sharp fragments, because there is danger of convulsion by
pricking a nerve, or the *periostium*. Sometimes the fragments of a broken bone keep themselves in their due place:
they also oft times fly forth thereof, so that one of them
gets above another; which when it happens, you may perceive an inequality by the depression of the one part and

Fractures at joynts dangerous.

Hipp. sect. 18. & 19. sect. i. de fracturis.

Ligations conduce to the hand-somnes of a Callus.

the bunching forth of the other, as also paine by the pricking: besides also the member is made shorter than it was,
and than the sound member on the opposite side is, and
more swolne by the contraction of the muscles towards

Extension
must pre-
sently bee
made after
the bone is
broken.

their originall. Wherefore when a bone is broken, if you
perceive anie thing so depressed, presently putting your
hand on both sides above and below, stretch forth the bone
as forcibly as you can; for otherwise, the muscles and
nerves, stretched and contracted, will never of their owne
accord suffer the bones to be restored to their proper seat
and themselves. This extension must bee performed in the
first dayes, for afterwards there will happen inflammation:
which being present, it is dangerous to draw the nerves and
tendons too violently; for hence would ensue an impostume, convulsion, gangrene and mortification. Therefore

Sent. 36.
sect. 3. de
fract.

Hippocrates forbids you to defer such extension untill the
third, or fourth day. Fractures are thought dangerous,
whose fragments are great, and fly out, especially in these
bones which are filled with marrow on the inside. When
broken or dislocated bones cannot be restored to themselves and their naturall place, the part wasts for want of
nourishment; both for that the naturall site of the veines,
arteries and nerves is perverted, as also because the part it
selfe lyes immoveable, or scarce moveable: whereby it
commeth to passe, that the spirits doe not freely flow
thereto, as neyther the nutritive juice commeth thither in
sufficient plentie. When the dislocated or broken member

In inflamma-
tions the re-
storing of
the bone
must not bee
attempted.

is troubled with any great inflammation, it is doubtfull
whether or no a convulsion will happen, if wee attempt to
restore it, or the parts thereof to their seat: therefore it is
better, if it may bee done, to deferre the reducing thereof so
long, untill the humor which possesses the part be dissolved,
the tumor abated, and the bitternesse of paine mitigated.

The generall cure of broken and dislocated bones.

To cure a broken and dislocated bone, is to restore it to
its former figure and site. For the performance whereof,

the Surgeon must propose three things to himselfe: The first is, to restore the bone to its place: The second is, that he containe or stay it being so restored: The third is, that he hinder the increase of maligne symptomes and accidents; or else if they doe happen, that then he temper and correct their present malignitie. Such accidents are paine, inflammation, a feaver, abscesse, gangrene and sphacell. For the first intention, you may easily restore a broken or dislocated bone, if presently, as soon as the mischance is got, or else the same day, you endeavour to restore it: for the bitternesse of paine or inflammation, which may trouble the patient, is not as yet verie great, neyther is the contraction of the muscles upwards as yet very much or stubborne. Therefore first of all, the Patient with his whole bodie, but especially with the broken or dislocated part, as also the Surgeon, must bee in some place which hath good and sufficient light. Then let trusty and skilfull attendants be there, good ligatures, and also, if need so require, good engines. His friends which are present, let them see and hold their peace, neyther say, nor do any thing which may hinder the Worke of the Surgeon. Then putting one hand above, that is, towards the center of the body, and the other below, as neare as hee can to the part affected, let him stretch forth the member: for if you lay your hand any distance from the part affected, you wil hurt the sound part by too much compression, neyther will you much avayle your selfe by stretching it at such a distance. But if you only endeavour below with your hand or ligature, assisting to make extension thereof, it will be dangerous if there bee nothing above which may withstand or hold, lest that you draw the whole bodie to you. This being done, according as I have delivered, it is fit the Surgeon make a right or straight extension of the part affected: for when the bone is eyther broken or out of joynt, there is a contraction of the muscles towards their originall, and consequently of the bones by them, as it is observed by Galen. Wherefore it is impossible to restore the bones to their

Three things to be performed in curing broken and dislocated bones.

How to put the bones in their places.

Hipp. sent. 60. sect. 2. de fract.

Ad sent. 1. sect. 1. de fract.

former seat, without the extension of the muscles. But the
part being thus extended, the broken bones will sooner and
more easily be restored to their former seate. Which being
restored, you shall presently with your hand presse it
downe, if there be any thing that bunches or stands out.
And lastly, you shall binde it up, by applying boulsters and
splints as shall bee fit. But if the bone bee dislocated or
forth of joynt, then presently after the extension thereof,
it will be requisite to bend it somwhat about, and so to

When in-
struments or
engins are
necessary.

draw it in. The Surgeon is sometimes forced to use engines
for this worke, especially if the luxation be inveterate, if
the broken or luxated bones be great; and that in strong
and rustick bodies, and such as have large joynts: for that
then there is need of greater strength, than is in the hand
of the Surgeon alone. For, by how much the muscles of
the Patient are the stronger, by so much will they bee contracted more powerfully upwards towards their originals.
Yet have a care that you extend them not too violently,
lest by rending and breaking asunder the muscles and
nerves, you cause the forementioned symptomes, paine,
convulsion, a palsie and gangrene: all which sooner happen

What bodies
are sooner
hurt by vio-
lent exten-
sion.

to strong and aged bodies, than to children, eunuches,
women; youthes, and generally all moyst bodies, for that
they are lesse hurt by violent extension and pulling, by
reason of their native and much humiditie and softnesse.
For thus skins of leather, moystened with any liquor, are
easily retched and drawn out as one pleaseth: but such as
are dry & hard, being lesse tractable, will sooner rend and
teare, than stretch further out. Therefore the Surgeon shall
use a meane in extending and drawing forth of members,
as shall be most agreeable to the habits of the bodies. You

Signes of a
bone well set.

may know the bone is set, and the setting performed as is
fit, if the paine be asswaged; to wit, the fibres of the
muscles, and the other parts being restored to their former
site, and all compression, which the bones moved out of
their places have made, being taken away; if, to your feeling there bee nothing bunching out, nor rugged, but the

surface of the member remaine smooth and equall; and lastly, if the broken or dislocated member compares with its opposite in the composure of the joynts, as the knees and ancles answer justly and equally in length and thicknesse. For which purpose it must not suffice the Surgeon to view it once, but even as often as he shall dresse it. For it may happen, that the bone which is well set, may by some chance, as by the Patients unconsiderate turning himselfe in his bed, or as it were a convulsive twitching of the members or joynts whilest he sleepes, the muscles of their owne accord contracting themselves towards their originals, that the member may againe fall out; and it will give manifest signes thereof by renewing the paine, by pressing or pricking the adjacent bodies: which paine will not cease, before it bee restored to its place: and hereof the Surgeon ought to have diligent care. For if, whilest the *Callus* is in growing, one bone ride over another, the bone it selfe will afterwards be so much the shorter, and consequently the whole member; so that if this errour shall happen in a broken legge, the Patient will halt ever after, to his great griefe, and the Surgeons shame. Wherefore the Patient shall take heed, as much as in him lyes, that he stirre not the broken member, before that the *Callus* be hardened. Such diligent care needes not bee had in dislocations. For these once set, and artificially bound up, doe not afterwards so easily fall forth as broken bones.

Causes and signes of the relapse of a set bone.

The second scope is, that the bones which shall be restored may bee firmly kept in their state and place. That shall be done by Bandages; as ligatures, boulsters, and other things, whereof hereafter we shall make particular mention. Hither tend proper and fit medicines, to wit, applying of oyle of Roses with the whites of Egges, and the like repelling things; and then resolving medicines, as the present necessity shall require. It will be convenient, to moysten your rowlers and boulsters in oxycrate for this purpose, or else in Rose vinegar, if the Fracture be simple, or with red wine, or the like liquor warme (in Galens opinion) if a

Ad sent. 21. sect. 1. de fract.

wound bee joyned to the fracture; and it will be fit to moysten fractures oftner in Summer: For so the part is strengthened, the defluxion being repelled, whereby the inflammation and paine are hindred. You must desist from humecting and watering the part when the symptomes are past, lest you retard the generating of a *Callus*; for which you must labour by these meanes which wee shall hereafter declare. To this purpose also conduces the rest and lying of the part in its proper figure and site accustomed in health, that so it may the longer remaine in the same place unstirred. Besides also, it is expedient then only to dresse the part, when it is needfull, & with those things that are requisite, shunning, as much as may be, inflammation and paine. That figure is thought the best, which is the middle, that is, which containes the muscles in their site, which is without paine; so that the Patient may long endure it without labour or trouble. All these things being performed, the Patient must be asked, Whether the member be bound up too strait? If he answer, No, (unlesse peradventure a little upon the fracture or luxation, for there it is fit it should bee more straitly bound) then may you know that the binding is moderate. And this same first ligation is to bee kept in fractures without loosing for three or foure dayes space, unlesse peradventure paine urge you to the contrary. In dislocations the same binding may bee kept for seven or eight daies, unlesse by chance some symptome may happen, which may force us to open it before that time: for the Surgeon must with all his art have a care to prohibite the happening of evill accidents and symptomes, which, how he may bring to passe, shall bee declared in the following Chapter.

What the middle figure is, and why best.

Fit time for loosing of Ligatures in fractures and dislocations.

By what meanes you may performe the third intention in curing fractures and dislocations, which is, the hindring and correction of accidents and symptomes.

That we may attaine unto this third scope, it is requisite we handle as gently and without paine, as we may, the

Foure choice meanes to hinder accidents.

broken or dislocated member; we drive away the defluxion ready to fall downe upon the part by medicines, repelling the humour, and strengthning the part; wee, by appointing a good diet, hinder the begetting of excrements in the bodie, and divert them by purging and phlebotomie. But if these accidents be already present, we must cure them according to the kinde and nature of each of them: for they are various. Amongst which is reckoned itching, which in the beginning torments the Patient: this ariseth from a collection and suppression of subacride vapours, arising from the blood, and other humors under the skin. Whence a light biting, which causeth a simple itch, or else a more grievous and acride one, from whence (in Galens opinion) proceeds a painefull itching. Wherefore such matter, as the cause, being evacuated, all itching ceaseth. But this cannot easily and freely be evacuated and breathed out, because the pores of the part are shut up, and as it were oppressed with the burden of the emplaisters, boulsters, and ligatures, which are put about the part. Hereunto may be added, that the part its selfe doth not so perfectly performe and enjoy its wonted faculties and actions: by which it commeth to passe, that the heat thereof is more languide than may suffice to discusse the fuliginous matter there collected. Wherefore it will be convenient to loose the ligatures everie third day, that, as by loosing their tyes, their sanious and fuliginous excrements, shut up under the skinne, may freely passe forth, lest in continuance they should fret and ulcerate it; as it happens to most of those who provide not for it by loosing their ligatures. Besides also, the part must bee long fomented with hot water alone, or else with a decoction of sage, chamomile, roses, and melilote made in wine and water: for long fomenting attenuates and evacuates, but shorter fils and mollifies, as it is delivered by Hippocrates. Also gentle frictions, performed with your hand, or a warme linnen cloath upwards, to the right side and left, and circularly to everie side, are good. But if the skinne be already risen into blisters, they must be cut, lest

The causes and differences of itching.

Ad sent. 4. sect. 1. de fract.

Remedies against the itching.

the matter contained thereunder may corrode and ulcerate the skinne: then must the skinne be annointed with some cooling and drying medicine; as, *Ung. album Camphoratum Rhasis, Desiccativum rubrum, unguentum rosatum sine aceto*; adding thereto the pouder of a rotten poste, or prepared *Tutia*, or the like. Other accidents more grievous than these, doe often happen, but we will treat of them hereafter. But if the scales of the bone underneath bee quite severed from the whole, then must they be presently taken forth, especially if they prick the muscles: But if the bone be broken into splinters, and so prominent out of the wounded flesh as that it cannot be restored into its seat, it must be cut off with your cutting mallets, or parrats beake, as occasion shall offer its selfe. In the interim, you must have a care that the part enjoy perspiration, and by change of place and rising, now and then it may be as it were ventilated: also you must see that it be not over-burdened, neyther too strait bound, otherwise it will be apt to inflammation.

Hipp. sent. 46. sect. 3. de fract.

OF DISLOCATIONS
OR
LUXATIONS

Of the kinds and manners of Dislocations.

A DISLOCATION is the departure or falling out of the head of a bone from its proper cavitie, into an unaccustomed place beside nature, hindring voluntarie motion. There is another kinde of Luxation, which is caused by a violent distention, and as it were a certaine divarication, and dilatation, or extension into length and breadth of the ligaments, and all the nervous bodies, which containe, strengthen, and binde together the joynts. Thus those who have beene tormented and racked, have that thick ligament which is in the inner cavitie of the huckle bone too violently extended: Those who have suffered the Strappado, have the ligaments, encompassing the articulation of the Arme-bone, with the shoulder-blade, forcibly and violently distended. Such also is their affect whose foot is strained by slipping. There is a third kinde of Luxation, when as those bones which are joyned contiguous, and one (as it were) bound to the sides of another, gape or flye asunder: as in the Arme, when the ell parts from the wand; in the legge, when the one focile flyes from the other: yet this may be referred to the second sort of dislocations, because it happens not without dilatation, or else the breaking of the ligaments. There is also a fourth added to these, as when the *Epiphyses* and heads of bones

[marginal notes:] What a Luxation properly so called is.

What a Luxation not properly so called is.

The third kind of Dislocation.

The fourth.

are plucked from the bone whereon they were placed or fastened: which unproperly called kinde of Luxation, hath place chiefly in the bones of yong people, and it is knowne by the impotencie of the part, and by the noise and grating together of the crackling bones when they are handled. Now the bones of yong folks are also incident to another casualtie: for as the bones of old people are broken by violence by reason of their drinesse and hardnesse, thus the bones of children are bended or crooked in by reason of their naturall softnesse and humiditie.

Of the differences of Dislocations.

What Luxa-
tions are
simple.
What com-
pound.

Some Dislocations are simple, others compound. We terme them simple which have no other preternaturall affect joyned with them; and such compound, as are complicated with one or more preternaturall affects; as when a dislocation is associated with a wound, fracture, great paine, inflammation, and an abscesse. For, through occasion of these we are often compelled so long to let alone the luxation, untill these bee remitted of themselves, or by

What a
complete
Luxation is.

our art. Some Dislocations are complete and perfect, as when the bone wholly fals out of its cavitie: othersome are unperfect, as when it is only lightly moved, and not wholly fallen out; wherfore we only call them subluxations or

What a sub-
luxation or
straine.

strains. Differences of Luxations are also drawne from the place: for sometimes the bone is wrested forwards, otherwhiles backwards, upwards, downwards; somewhiles it may be wrested, according to all these differences of site, and otherwhiles onely according to some of them. Differences are also taken from the condition of the dislocated Joynt in greatnesse and littlenesse, from the superficiarie or deepe excavation of the *sinus* or hollownesse; and lastly from the time, as if it be lately done, or of some long continuance. I have judged it fit to set downe all these, for that there are severall indications of curing, according to the varietie of each of these, as we shall teach hereafter.

Of the causes of Dislocations.

There are three general causes of Luxations, internall, externall, and hereditarie. The internall are excrementitious humors and flatulencies, which, settling into the joynts with great force and plentie, doe so make slipperie, soften & relaxe the ligaments which binde together the bones, that they easily fall out of their cavities; or else they so fill and distend these ligaments, and make them so short, that being contracted, they also contract the *appendices* of the bones from whence they arise, and so pluck them from the bone whereon they are placed, or else draw the heads of the bones out of their cavities, chiefly if the violence of a noxious humor doth also concurre, which possessing and filling up the cavities of the joynts, puts them from their seats, as it oft times happens to the joynt of the hip by Sciaticaes, and to the *Vertebræ* of the spine, by whose Luxation people become gibbous, or otherwise crooked. But externall causes of Dislocations are, fals from high, bruising and heavie blowes, the Rack, Strappado, slipping in going, and all such like things, which may force the heads of the bones to fly out of their seats, or cavities, which also happens somtimes to infants in their birth, when as they are too carelesly and violently drawne forth by the Midwife, so that eyther their armes or legges are put out of joynt. Hereditarie causes are such as the Parents transfuse into their off-spring: hence it is, that crooked not necessarily, but often times, are generated by crooked, and lame by lame. The truth whereof is evident by daily experience. Besides also Hippocrates himselfe averres, that infants in the very wombe may have their Joynts dislocated by a fall, blow and compression, & by the too much humidity and loosenes of the Joynts: whence also we see many crooke legg'd and footed from their nativitie; so that none need marvell or make any doubt hereof. We have read it observed by Galen *In librum de Artic.* that children may have impostumes in their mothers wombs, which may cast forth

Internall causes of dislocations.

Externall causes.

Hereditary causes.

Sect. 3. sent. 88. & 94 sect. 82. 4. sent. 3. & 4. lib. de art.

Children may have Impostumes in their mothers wombs.

quitture,[1] the ulcers being opened of their own accord, and
be cicatrized by the only benefit of nature. It also happens
to many from their first conformation, that the cavities of
their Joynts are lesse deprest than they should bee, and that
their verges are more dilated than they ought to be; whereby it happens that the heads of the bones can the lesse enter
into them. It fals out, that othersome have the ligaments,
appointed by nature for fastening together the bones of the
joynt, whether inserted or placed about, so weake, that
from their first originall they are not of sufficient strength,
or else abound with much phlegme, eyther bred together
with them, or flowing from some other place; so that by
their too much slipperinesse they lesse faithfully containe
the knittings or articulations of the bones. In all these, as the
bones are easily dislocated, so they may presently be easily
restored without the assistance of a Surgeon, as I have
sometimes observed in some.

The signes of dislocations.

The com-
mon signe
of all dis-
locations.

Some of the signes whereby we come to the knowledge
of a luxated bone, are common to all dislocations; others
are proper only to severall Luxations. It is a common signe,
that there is alwaies a tumor in that part whereto the bone
runnes, and a hollownesse on that side from whence it is
flowne. Now the proper signes shall be shewed, when as
we come to treat of the particular kindes of Luxations. We
know a perfect Dislocation by the lost action of the part,
that is to say, the lost motion; paine also breeds a suspicion
of a dislocation: for the head of the bone, which (moved
out of its place) is forced into another, presses the flesh, and
distends the nerves also moved out of their place. Hereto
also conduces the comparing of the sound joynt with that
which is hurt, in which collation, it is fit the sound part,
which is compared with the hurt, be no waies, neyther by
nature nor any accident, wronged, nor deformed, nor
withered or decayed, nor swolne above measure, otherwise

[1] i.e. a purulent discharge.

it may cozen and deceive you, if you bee lesse warie.
Labour and difficultie of action in moving, is a signe of an
uncomplete Luxation, or strain. Now we thus know, that   Signes of an
the ligaments, serving to the connexion of the articulations,   unperfect
are extended and relaxed, if the head of the bone, pressed   dislocation.
with your fingers, be easily driven unto the contrary part,
and suddenly flye thence backe againe; if thrusting your
finger into the joynt, it easily enter, nothing resisting it, as
though all were empty within; if the motion be difficult,
or none at all.

Of Prognosticks to be made upon luxations.

All Joynts may bee perverted or luxated, but all of them   What luxa-
cannot in like manner be restored. For the head may be   tions be
dislocated, but therupon present death ensues, by reason of   uncureable.
the compression of the whole spinall marrow presently at
the originall thereof; such also is the dislocation of a *vertebra*
of the spine, and of the Jaw-bone, which, slipped forth on
both sides, hath caused inflammation, and a great tumor
before that it be set. The bones of other Joynts, as they are
more or lesse dislocated, and moved out of their seats, so
may they bee more easily or difficultly restored. For, by   Why those
how much they are the lesse moved out of their places,   bones which
by so much they are the more quickly, and by how much   are hardly
they are the further, by so much they are the more slowly   dislocated,
and difficultly set. Also an indication, taken from the figure   be set.
of the luxated bone, gives a signe of the easie or hard
restoring of the dislocation; as in the Arme, by how much
the bones be the more easily dislocated, by so much once
luxated they are the more easily restored. Bones doe not
easily fall out of joynt in fleshie bodies; but when they
chance to be put out, they are not easily got in againe. For
in such, the articulation is straitly on everie side held in by
the thicknesse of the muscles, and the plenty of the fat
lying thereabouts. On the contrarie, such as are leane,
especially those who formerly have beene more fat, have
their joynts more laxe, whereby it comes to passe, that

their bones may easily be put forth of joynt: besides also, through the default of the digestive facultie, they have their joynts replete with mucous humors; whence it is, that the heads of the bones, as standing in a slipperie place, are the

Sect. 1. *de artic. sent.* 29.
lesse stable, as it is recorded by Hippocrates. But slender bodies, which are naturally dry, compact and dense, have their muscles and ligaments more strong and dry; wherefore their bones are the more difficultly displaced; and

Celsus lib. 8. *cap.* 11.
displaced, the more difficultly set. Some bones, joyned amongst themselves, doe sometimes flye asunder, as when the shoulder blade flyes from the collar-bone at the *Acromion*, and in the Arme the Ell from the Wand, and in the Legge the one focile from the other, and the Heele-bone from the Ancle. Bones thus separated will never be joyned together againe, will never recover their former comely figure, never their strength of action. For, then it most usually happens, that the ligaments are either broke asunder, or else resolved and become laxe. Those whose bones are dislocated by an externall cause, they, after they be set, may easily fall out againe, for that the ligaments, moystened and bedewed with an excrementitious humor, cannot firmely hold them: oft times the ligaments are not wholly broken, but onely in some portion thereof; and hence the action of the part either perishes, or is debilitated. Also that dislocation is uncureable, when as the ligaments, steeped and swolne up with an excrementitious humiditie, are so much shortened and contracted in their length, as they have acquired in their breadth: and thus they draw away and plucke off the *appendices* of the bones from whence

Why the plucking of an *appendix* from a bone is uncureable.
they arise, and by reason the bone and the *appendix* doe enter and receive each other by manie cavities and prominencies, therefore they cannot, by how skilfull hand soever they be handled, be againe fitly placed and put together. Old and inveterate dislocations, wherin a tough humor possessing the cavitie is concrete in stead of the head of the bone, are not to be restored; as neither when the heads of the luxated bones have by continuall attrition

made themselves a new cavitie in the neighbouring bone: neither if they be restored, is the restitution firme and of continuance; because the naturall cavitie is possessed by another matter, and the new made neare thereto cannot well and faithfully containe the received head of the bone. Those who have their shoulder dislocated, may use their hand for many actions, as well as the opposite sound hand; for the weight of the bodie is not sustained by the hands, as it is by the legs. And by how much the hand is the more exercised, by so much the arme becoms the more corpulent. Contrarily, if the thigh-bone bee dislocated, especially if it bee wrested inwards, the whole legge quickly decayes by an *atrophia*, because the part doth absolutely lose all motion: for by the opinion of Hippocrates, the performance of the proper action encreases strength, and makes the part in better plight; but idlenesse debilitates and makes it leane. If a great wound and fracture bee joyned with a luxation, there is danger, lest while wee use extension for restoring the part, we draw the nerves too violently, and so break the nerves, veines and arteries, whence would ensue feare of inflammation, convulsion, and other maligne symptoms. Wherefore Hippocrates judges it better in such a concourse and complication of preternaturall affects, absolutely not to meddle at all with the setting of the dislocated bone: for, by attempting the restitution, certaine death; but by omitting it only lamenesse is to be feared. Everie dislocation must be restored before inflammation come; but if it be already present, you must presently be carefull to take it away. For other things, let the Patient rest, lest if the affect be irritated, the increase and excesse of paine cause a convulsion, gangrene, and lastly death, as I remember I have somtimes observed. Therfore when inflammation, and other maligne symptoms shall be mitigated and corrected, then may you endeavour to restore the luxation, especially if the habit of the bodie and member affected may admit it. For if the bodie be slender, delicate and tender, then the restitution will bee more

Hipp. sent. 88. *sect.* 3. *de art.*

Sent. 10. *sect.* 5. *lib.* 6. *epid.* & *sect.* 3. *de art. sent.* 88.

You must not endevour to set an inflamed joynt.

speedy and facile. But on the contrarie, more difficult, if it be grosse and compact; And let thus much suffice for prognosticks in Luxations.

Of the generall cure of Dislocations.

Five inten-
tions in
curing dislo-
cations.

For all that I have heretofore delivered the generall methode of curing Fractures and dislocations, yet it shall not bee unprofitable to repeat here in this place, those things which may be accommodated to this Treatise of curing Luxations. Now he that will cure Dislocations, must have regard to five intentions, which it will be fitting to performe in order. The first is, of Holding; The second, of Drawing or Extending; The third, of Forcing in; The fourth, of Placing in convenient figure and site; The fifth, of Correcting the concomitant, or following symptomes.

The benefit
of holding
the member
in disloca-
tions.

The first scope, which we said was of Holding, is meant eyther of the whole body, or else of some part thereof only. The whole bodie must bee holden by the strong embracement of your servant or attendant, when as the shoulder, the *vertebræ*, or the thigh-bones are dislocated. But in the dislocation of the Collar-bone, elbow, hand, knee, or foote and legge, it is sufficient onely to hold the part straitly in your hands. There is necessitie of holding eyther the bodie, or else some part thereof, lest, while the dislocated bone is extended, the whole bodie follow by continuance of parts, if there be nothing which may hinder: for if the bodie should follow him that drawes or extends, all the workmasters labour and endeavour to restore it, is to no purpose.

The use of
extension.

The use of the second scope, that is, of Drawing or Extending, is, that there may be a free space and distance betweene the luxated bones, by which distance the dislocated bone may the more freely be forced into its cavitie. But the manner of drawing or extending is different in quantity and manner, according to the various strength of the muscles and ligaments, and dislocation of the bones to this or that part. Therefore this worke is almost alwaies performed by the hands; which when they cannot suffice, we

must use the assistance of instruments and engins, whose
figures you shall see hereafter delineated. But that you may
not doe amisse, you may so farré use extension, untill the
head of the bone be brought just against its cavitie. When
the Surgeon hath brought it to this passe, then must he
hasten to the third intention, which is, to put the head of
the bone first moved and gently bended, into its cavitie.
For hee must have a speciall care, that hee force it no other
way than into its proper cavity: for it would be dangerous,
lest he should turne it from one extreme into another, and
the bone, for examples sake, of the thigh, which was dislocated into the forepart by too violent forcing, by exceeding the middle cavitie, may be driven and dislocated into
the hinder part. To shun this, the bone shall be put backe
the same way that it fell out, which may bee easily done
in fresh and late happening dislocations. We understand
that the bone is set by the noyse, or as it were a popp, or
sound like that, which solid and sounding bodies, being
fully and forcibly thrust into their cavities, do make; by
the similitude and consent in figure, magnitude and all conformation of the affected part with the sound, and lastly,
by the mitigation of the paine. The fourth scope, which is
of the convenient site of the part, must bee so fulfilled, that
the bone after it is set may bee kept in its cavity, and not
flye forth againe. Wherefore if the arme be dislocated, it
shall be carried bound up in a scarfe: if the thigh, knee,
legge, or foote be luxated, they shall be fitly layd in a bed;
but in the *interim* the Surgeon, presently after hee hath set
them, shall have a care, that the affected joynt be wrapped
about with stoups and clothes, or compresses steeped in
rose vinegar, and spred with convenient medicines; then
let it be bound with an artificiall deligation, rowling the
ligatures unto the part contrary to that whereto the dislocated bone flew. For the which purpose thicker boulsters
shall be there applied whence the bone came out, otherwise
there will be some danger, lest it should be againe displaced: when these things are done, he shall for foure or

The manner of setting it, or putting it into its place.

Signes that the bone is set.

The benefit of fit placing the member.

The manner of binding up the set joynt.

five dayes space meddle with nothing about the Dislocation, unlesse paine, or some such like symptome happen.
For then the fifth scope will call us from that cessation and
rest, which is, to correct the symptomes and complicate
affections, as paine, inflammation, a wound, fracture, and
others, wherof wee have spoken abundantly in our Treatise
of Fractures. Before wee attempt to set inveterate dislocations, wee must endevour to humect[1] the ligaments, tendons

**The cure of
inveterate
luxations.**

and muscles by fomentations, cataplasmes, emplaisters, liniments, and other remedies, that so these parts may be more
obedient to the Surgeons hand: then must the dislocated
bones be moved, with a gentle motion up and down, to
and againe, that by this meanes the excrementitious humor,
which by continuance of time hath flowed downe, may
waxe hot, be attenuated, resolved or made slipperie, and
also the fibres of the muscles, ligaments, and nervous bodies,
placed about the joynt for the defence thereof, may be
loosed, that so they may presently be more freely extended.
But if a great swelling, paine and inflammation urge, we
must first think of asswaging and curing them, then of the
restoring the Dislocation.

The description of certaine engines, serving for the restoring of Dislocations.

Before I come to the particular kinds of Dislocations,
I thinke it not amisse to describe three sorts of Bandages,

**These liga-
tures are not
for deliga-
tion, but
extension.**

and give you their figures, as those which are most fit to
hold and extend Dislocations. The first Ligature, designed
by this letter *A*, is made for holding the member. The
second, marked with the letter *B*, is fit for drawing or
extension, and consists of one knot. The third, whereto the
letter *C* is put, consisting of two knots, is to hold or binde
more straitly.

I have thought good also to delineate the following
Engine, made for to draw and extend more powerfully,
when the hand will not serve. It is made like a Pulley,

[1] i.e. to moisten.

marked with these letters *D D*. Within this there lye hid three wheeles, through whose furrowes runnes the rope which is to be drawne, marked with this letter *H*. At the ends of the Pulley are hooks fastened, the one of which is

The delineation of the three Ligatures.

to fasten the Pulley to a Poste, the other is to draw the ligature fastened to the part. The Boxes or Cases wherein the Pulley is kept, is marked with *B B*. Their covers are marked with *A A*. A screw pin which may be twined, and so fastened to a Poste, that so one of the ends of the Pulley may be hooked thereto, is signed with *C*. A Gimlet (marked by *F*.) to make a hole in a Poste, so to let in the screw pin. You may see all these things exprest in this following figure.

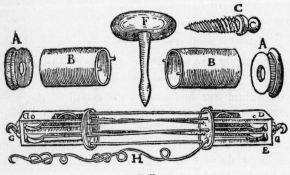

A Pulley.

Some Practitioners in stead of this Pulley make use of the hereafter described Instrument, which they terme *Manubrium versatile*, or a Hand-vice. The end therof is fashioned like a Gimblet, and is to be twined into a Poste. Within

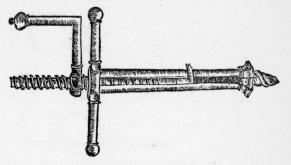

Manubrium versatile, or, *A Hand-vice*.

that handle lyes a screw with a hooked end, whereto the string or ligature must be fastened. Now the screw-rod or male-screw runnes into the female by the twining about of the handle: and thus the ligature is drawne as much as will suffice, for the setting the dislocated bone.

OF CATARACTS

By what signes ripe and curable cataracts may bee discerned from unripe and uncurable ones.

IF the sound eye being shut, the pupill of the sore or suffused eye, after it shall be rubbed with your thumbe, bee presently dilated and diffused, and with the like celerity returne into the place, figure, colour and state, it is thought by some to shew a ripe and confirmed cataract. But an unripe and not to bee couched, if the pupill remaine dilated and diffused for a long while after. But it is a common signe of a ripe, as also more dense and consequently uncurable suffusion, to bee able to see nor distinguish no visible thing beside light and brightnesse; for to discerne other objects sheweth that it is not yet ripe. Therefore the sound eye being shut and pressed, the pupill of the other rubbed with your thumbe, is dilated, enlarged, swelleth and is more diffused; the visive spirits by this compression being as it were forced from the sound into the sore eye. But these following cataracts are judged uncurable, that is, such as are great, such as when the eye-lid is rubbed are nothing dilated or diffused, whose pupill becommeth no broader by this rubbing: for hence you may gather that the stopping or obstruction is in the opticke nerve, so that how cunningly and well soever the cataract bee couched, yet will the Patient continue blind; you shall do no more good in couching a cataract, which is in an eye consumed and wasted with a *Phthisis*. Also that cataract is uncurable which is occasioned by a most grievous disease, to wit, by most bitter and cruell paines of the head, or by a violent blow. Such as are of a plaister-like, green, blacke, livid, citrine and quicksilver-like colour, are usually uncurable. On the contrary, such as are of a Chesnut colour, or of a skye or sea-water colour, with some little whitnesse, yeeld great hope of a happy and successefull cure.

Uncurable Cataracts.

Curable Cataracts.

Of the couching a Cataract.

After you shal know by the forementioned signes, that the Cataract is curable, it remains that you attempt the couching thereof, but so, that there be nothing which may hinder. For if the paine of the head, cough, nauseousnes or vomiting at that time trouble the patient, you shal then bestow your labour in vaine: Wherefore you must expect untill these symptomes be gone. Then make choice of a season fitting for that purpose, that is, in the decrease of the moon, when the aire is not troubled with thunder nor lightening, and when as the Sunne is not in Aries, because

When to couch a Cataract.

that signe hath dominion over the head. Then let the Surgeon consult a Physitian whether purging or bloud-letting be convenient for the Patient, so to resist plethoricke symptomes, otherwaies ready to yeeld matter for relapse. Two dayes after you must make choice of a place furnished with indifferent or competent light, and the Patient being fasting shall be placed in a strait chaire, so that the light may not fall with the beames directly upon him, but sidewise. The eye which shall bee cured must bee made more steddy, by laying and binding wooll upon the other: Then the Surgeon shall seate and place himselfe directly against the Patient upon a seat somewhat higher, and bidding the Patient put his hands downe to his girdle, he shall hold the patients legges betweene his knees. One shall stand at the Patients backe who shall hold his head and keepe it from stirring; for by a little stirring hee may lose his sight for ever. Then must you prepare and make ready your needle, and thrust it often into some strong thicke cloth, that it may bee as it were smoothe by this motion, and for the performance of the worke in hand with the lesse paine somewhat warmed. It must bee made of iron or steele, and not of gold or silver, it must be also flatted on the sides, and sharpe pointed, that so it may the better pierce into the eye, and wholly couch the Cataract once taken hold of; and lest it should slip in the Surgeons hand, and be lesse steddy, it shall bee put into a handle, as you may see by the following figure.

The place.

The needle.

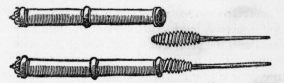

A needle inserted in a handle for the couching of Cataracts.

All things being thus in a readinesse, you must bid the patient to turne the sight of his eye towards his nose, and the needle must be boldly thrust (for it is received in a place that is voyde, and onely filled with spirits) directly by the coat *Adnata*, in the middle space between the lesser corner & the horny coat, just against the midst of the Cataract, yet so, as that you hurt no vein of the *Adnata*, & then by stirring it as it were diversly untill it come to the midst of the pupill and suffusion. When it is come thither, the needle must bee inclined from above downewards to the suffusion, and there to be stirred gently untill by little and little it couch or bring downe the Cataract as whole as may be beneath the compasse of the pupill; let him still follow it though couched with his needle, and somewhat violently depresse, and keep it down for some short space, that so it may rest and stay in that lower place whether it is depressed. The Surgeon shall try whether it firmely remaine there or no, bidding the patient presently to move his eye; For if it remaine constantly so, and doe not returne againe, the cure is perfect. Then must the needle be lifted up by little and little, neither must it presently be taken forth, that if the Cataract should beare up, or rise againe, that it might againe, and so often (whilst the worke is yet hot, and all things in a readinesse) be couched towards the lesser corner, untill it be fully and surely hid. Then must you draw backe the needle gently, and after the same manner as you put it in; lest if you use not moderation, you bring backe the Cataract, from whence you couched it, or grievously offend the crystalline humour, the prime instrument of sight, or the pupill with danger of dilating thereof. Some as soone as the worke is done, give the patient something in his hand to looke upon: but *Paulus* approves not thereof, for hee feares lest his endeavouring or striving to see, may draw backe the Cataract. Wherefore it is more wisedome and better, presently after the drawing forth of the needle, to put on a soft ragge the white of an egge beaten in rose-water with a little choice alume, and so apply it to the eye and neighbouring parts for to binde and hinder the inflammation; then also you must together therewith bind up the

Gal. lib. 10. *de usu partium cap.* 5. *Cels. lib.* 7.

The signe of a Cataract well couched.

Lib. 6. *cap.* 21.

What to be done after the couching of a Cataract.

sound eye, lest by stirring to see, it might together there-with draw and move the sore eye, by reason of the sympathy and consent they mutually have by the opticke nerves. After all things are thus performed, the patient shall bee laid in a soft bed, & so placed, that his head may lye somwhat high; let him be laid far from noise, let him not speake, nor eate any hard thing that may trouble his jawes, wherefore let him feed upon liquid meats, as ponado, barly cream, cullisses, gellyes, reare egs, and other meates of the like nature. At the end of eight dayes the ligature that binds up his eyes shall be loosed, and his eyes washed with rose water, and putting on spectacles, or some taffaty, the patient shall by little and little accustome himselfe to the light, lest hee should bee offended by the sudden meeting with light. But if the suffusion, after some short while after, lift it selfe up againe, it must bee couched againe, but through a new hole, for the eye is pained and tender in the former place. It sometimes happens by the touch of the needle that the Cataract is not couched whole, but is broken into many peeces; then therefore each of them must be followed, and couched severally: if there be any very small particle which scapes the needle, it must bee let alone, for there is no doubt but that in processe of time it may be

Of a Cataract which is broken to pieces. dissolved by the force of the native heat. There are also some Cataracts which at the first touch of the needle are diffused & turne into a substance like to milke or troubled water, for that they are not throughly ripe, yet these put us in good hope of recovery, and it bee but for this, that they can never afterwards concrete into one body as before. Wherefore at the length they are also discussed by the strength of the native heat, and then the eye recovers its former splendor. If that any other symptomes come un-looked for, they shall be helped by new counsels and their appropriate remedies.

OF CUTTING FOR THE STONE

How to cut men for the taking out of the stone in the bladder.

SEEING wee cannot otherwise helpe such men as have stones in their bladders, we must come to the extreme remedy, to wit, cutting. But the patient must first be purged, and if the case require, draw some bloud; yet must you not immediately after this, or the day following hasten to the work, for the patient cannot but be weakened by purging & bleeding. Also it is expedient for some daies before to foment the privities with such things as relaxe and soften, that by their yeelding, the stone may the more easily be extracted. Now the cure is thus to be performed; The patient shall be placed upon a firm table or bench with a cloth many times doubled under his buttocks, and a pillow under his loynes & back, so that he may lie halfe upright with his thighs lifted up, and his legs and heels drawn back to his buttocks. Then shall his feet be bound with a ligature of three fingers breadth cast about his ankles, and with the heads thereof being drawn upwards to his neck, and cast about it, and so brought downewards, both his hands shall bee bound to his knees, as the following figure sheweth.

The patient thus bound, it is fit you have foure strong men at hand; that is, two to hold his armes, and other two who may so firmly and straightly hold the knee with one hand, and the foot with the other, that he may neither move his limmes, nor stirre his buttocks, but be forced to keep in the same posture with his whole body. Then the Surgeon shall thrust into the urinary passage even to the bladder, a silver or iron and hollow probe, annoynted with oyle, and opened or slit on the out side, that the point of the knife may enter thereinto, and that it may guide the

What to bee done before dissection.

How to lay the patient.

Why the probe must be slit on the out-side.

The figure of a man lying ready to be cut for the stone.

hand of the workman, and keep the knife from piercing any farther into the bodies lying thereunder. The figure of this probe is here exprest.

Probes with slits in their ends.

Why the seame of the *perinæum* must not be cut.

He shall gently wrest the probe, being so thrust in, towards the left side, and also he who standeth on the patients right hand, shall with his left hand gently lift up his Cods, that so in the free and open space of the left side of the *perinæum*, the Surgeon may have the more liberty to make the incision upon the probe which is thrust in and turned that way. But in making this incision, the Surgeon must be carefull that he hurt not the seame of the *perinæum* and fundament. For if that seame bee cut, it will not be easily consolidated, for that it is callous and bloudlesse, therefore the urine would continually drop forth this way. But if the wound be made too neare the fundament, there is danger, lest by forcible plucking forth of the stone he may break some of the hæmorrhoide veins, whence a

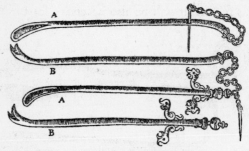

The figures of Guiders of two sorts.

bleeding may ensue, which is scarce to be stopped by any meanes, or that hee may rend the *sphincter* muscle, or body of the bladder, so that it can never be repaired. Therefore it must be made the space of two fingers from the funda-ment, according to the straightnesse of the fibres, that so it may be the more easily restored afterwards. Neither must the incision thus made exceed the bignesse of ones thumbe, for that it is afterwards enlarged by putting in the Crowes beake and the dilater, but more by the stone as it is plucked forth. But that which is cut, is neither so speedily nor easily healed up, as that which is torne. Then presently put into the wound some one of these silver instruments delineated here above, and called by the name of Guiders, for that they serve as guides to the other instruments which are to be put into the bladder; these are made with a round & prominent head, whereby it may bee put into the described

Where to make the wound to take forth the stone.

That which is torne is sooner healed than that which is cut.

cavity of the probe, and they are noted by these letters
A.A. then there are others marked with the letters B.B.
and called by the like name, and are to be put under the
former, being made forked at the end, that so it may, as it
were, embrace the end of the former.

Now the probe is to be drawne forth, and the Guiders
to be thrust and turned up and downe in the bladder, and
at length to be stayed there by putting in the pin; yet such
Guiders as want a pin are fitter for the hand, and are by
some called *spathæ*. Then must they be held betwixt the
Surgeons fingers. It will be also necessary for the Surgeon

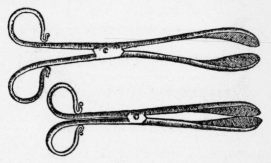

The effigies of an instrument called a Ducks bill.

to put another instrument called the Ducks bill between
the two Guiders into the capacity of the bladder; hee must
thrust it in somewhat violently, and dilate it so thrust in
with both his hands, turning it every way to enlarge the
wound as much as shall be sufficient for the admitting the
other instruments which are to be put into the bladder;
yet it is farre better for the patient, if that the wound may
with this one instrument be sufficiently dilated, and the
stone pulled forth with the same without the help of any
other.

Which if you have not in a readinesse, and the largeness
of the stone require more dilatation, then must you put in
this Dilater, for being put into the bladder, and the handle

pressed together, it will dilate the incision as much as you desire.

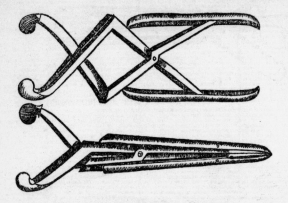

The figure of a Dilater shut and opened.

The wound by the helpe of this instrument being dilated as much as is sufficient, then put in the streight Ducks-bil! before described, or the crooked here exprest.

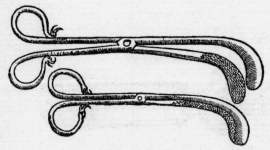

Crooked Forcipes *like a Ducks-bill.*

The stone may be sought & taken hold of with these instruments, and being taken hold on, the branches of the instrument shall bee tyed together, lest they should suffer that to slide away which they have once taken hold of. Neither shall the stone be suddenly plucked out, but easily

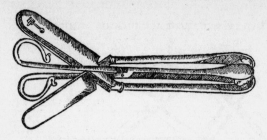

Winged instruments to hold the stone with the Ducks-beake.

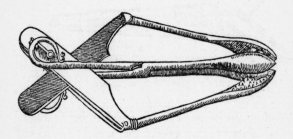

The figure of another.

The figure of another winged instrument, the end of whose handle is fastned by a screw, as also a bended iron plate which is marked with this letter A. for the firmer holding thereof.

shaken too & again, and at the length gently drawn forth. Yet you must beware that you doe not presse it too straightly in the *forceps*, lest you should breake it in pieces: Some, lest it should slip away, when they have once taken hold thereof, put their two fingers into the fundament, and put them above the stone that it may not fall out, nor slip backe againe, which I thinke conduceth much to the easie extraction of the stone. There are others who strengthen this comprehension by putting in on each side above and below these winged instruments, so that the stone can slip forth on no side.

After the stone is by these meanes drawne forth, observe diligently whether it be worne on any side, and as it were lævigated; for that happeneth by the wearing or rubbing of one or more stones upon it; yet there is no surer way to know this, than by searching with a *Cathæter*. The one end of the following instrument may supply the want of a *Cathæter* or probe, and the other may serve for a scoop or Cleanser.

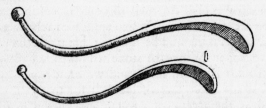

A cleanser or scoop whereby you may search whether there be any more stones behind, as also cleanse or purge the bladder from gravell, clots of bloud, and other such bodies, as use to remaine behind after the drawing forth of the stone.

For if other stones remaine behinde, they shall bee drawne forth as the former, which being done, the end of the instrument, which is crooked and hollowed like a scoop or spoone, shall bee thrust by the wound into the bladder, and therewith you shall gather together and take out what gravell soever, clotted bloud, and the like refuse as shall be

A note of more stones than one.

How to cleanse the bladder.

How to break a stone that cannot be taken out whole and at once.

there, for that they may yeeld matter for another stone. But if you find that the stone which is in the bladder be too great, so that it may not be plucked forth without great and fearfull rending of the bladder, it will be better to take hold thereof with this Crowes bill and so break it to peeces.

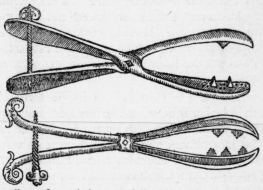

The effigies of a toothed Crowes-bill made neatly to breake greater stones, with a screw to force it together.

This Crowes bill hath onely three teeth, and those sharpe ones on the inside, of which two are placed above, and one below, which is the middle-most, so that it falleth between the two upper. When the stone is broken, all the peeces thereof must be taken forth, and we must have a speciall care, lest any piece thereof lye hid; for that in time, increased by the accesse of a tough and viscous matter, or conjoyned with other fragments by the interposition of the like matter as glew, may rise to a stone of a large bignesse.

OF BEZOAR

Of Bezoar, and Bezoarticke medicines.

FOR that we have made mention of Bezoar, in What is poison. treating of the remedies of poysons, I judge I shall not doe amisse, if I shall explaine, what the word meanes, and the reason thereof. Poyson absolutely taken is that which kils by a certaine specifick antipathy contrary to our nature. So an Antidote or Counter-poyson is by the Arabians in their mother tongue termed Bedezahar, as the preservers of life. This word is unknowne to the Greekes and Latines, and in use onely with the Arabians and Persians, because the thing it selfe first came from them, as it is plainely shewed by *Garcias ab horto*, Physician to the Vice-Roy of the Indies, in his history of the Spices and Simples of the East-Indies. In Persia (saith hee) and a certaine part of India is a certaine kinde of Goate called Pazain (wherefore in proper speaking, the stone should bee termed Pazar, of the word Pazain, that signifies a Goate; but wee corruptly terme it Bezar or Bezoar) the colour of this beast is commonly reddish, the height thereof indifferent, in whose stomack concretes the stone called Bezoar; it growes by A signe of true Bezoar. little and little about a straw or some such like substance in scailes like to the scailes of an onion, so that when as the first scaile is taken off, the next appeares more smooth and shining as you still take them away, the which amongst others is the signe of good Bezoar and not adulterate. This stone is found in sundry shapes, but commonly it resembles an Acorne or Date-stone; it is sometimes of a sanguine colour, and otherwhiles of a hony-like or yellowish colour, but most frequently of a blackish or dark greene, resembling the colour of mad Apples, or else of a Civet Cat. This stone hath no heart nor kernell in the midst, but powder in the cavity thereof, which is also of the same faculty. Now this stone is light, & not very hard, but so that it may easily be scraped, or rasped like alabaster, so that it will dissolve, being long macerated in water; at first it was common amongst us, and of no very great price, because our people who trafficked in Persia, bought it at an easie rate. But after that the faculties thereof were found out, it began to bee more rare and deare, and it was prohibited by an Edict from the King of the countrey, that no body should sell a Goate to the stranger Merchants, unlesse he first killed him, and tooke forth the stone, & brought it to the King. Of the notes by which this stone is tryed, (for there are many counterfeits brought hither) the first is already declared; the other is, it may bee blowne up by the breath, like an oxes hide; for if the wind breake through, and doe not stay in the density thereof, it is accounted counterfeit. They use it, induced thereto by our example, not onely against poysons, but also against the bites of venemous beasts. The richer sort of the Countrey purge twice a yeare, to wit, in March and September; and then, five daies together they take the powder of this stone macerated in Rose-water, the weight of ten graines at a time: for by this remedy they thinke their youth is preserved, as also the strength of their members. There be some who take the weight of thirty graines; yet the more wary exceed not twelve grains. The same author addeth that he useth it with very good successe in inveterate melancholy diseases as the itch, scab, tetters[1] & leprosie; therefore by the same reason it may well be given against a quartaine feaver. Besides, hee affirmeth for certaine that the powder conteined in the midst of the stone, put upon the bites of venemous beasts, presently freeth the patient from the danger of the poyson, as also applied to pestilent Carbuncles when they are opened, it drawes forth the venome. But because the small pocks and meazles are familiar in the Indies, and oft-times dangerous, it is there given with good successe, two graines

The use of Bezoar.

---

[1] i.e. a cutaneous eruption such as eczema.

each day in Rose-water. *Mathiolus* subscribeth to this *Lib. 5. in Dios. cap. 73.* opinion of *Garcias*, witnessing that hee hath found it by frequent experience, that this stone by much exceeds not only other simple medicines of this kind, but also such as are termed *theriacalia*, and what other Antidotes soever. Hereto also consents *Abdalanarach*; Wee (saith he) have seene the stone which they call Bezahar, with the sonnes of *Almirama* the observer of the Law of God; with which stone hee bought a stately and almost princely house at Corduba.

Some yeares agoe a certaine Gentleman, who had one of A history. these stones which hee brought out of Spaine, bragged before King *Charles* then being at Clermont in Auverne, of the most certaine efficacie of this stone against all manner of poysons. Then the King asked of mee, whether there were any Antidote which was equally and in like maner prevalent against all poisons? I answered, that nature could No one thing can be an Antidote against all poyson. not admit it; for neither have all poysons the like effects, neither doe they arise from one cause; for some worke from an occult and specifick property of their whole nature, others from some elementary quality which is predominant. Wherefore each must be withstood with its proper and contrary Antidote, as to the hot, that which is cold, and to that which assailes by an occult proprietie of forme, another which by the same force may oppugne it, and that it was an easie matter to make triall hereof on such as were condemned to bee hanged. The motion pleased the King; there was a Cooke brought by the Jailor who was to have been hanged within a while after for stealing two silver dishes out of his masters house. Yet the King desired first to know of him, whether hee would take the poison on this condition, that if the Antidote which was predicated to have singular power against all manner of poisons, which should bee presently given him after the poison, should free him from death, that then he should have his life saved. The Cooke answered chearfully, that he was willing to undergo the hazzard, yea, and greater matters, not only for to save his life, but to shun the infamy of the death he was like to be adjudged to. Therefore he then had poyson given him by the Apothecarie that then waited, and presently after the poyson, some of the Bezahar brought from Spain, which being taken down, within a while after hee began to vomit, and to avoid much by stoole with grievous torments, and to cry out that his inward parts were burnt with fire. Wherefore, being thirsty, and desiring water, they gave it him; an houre after, with the good leave of the Jaylor, I was admitted to him; I find him on the ground going like a beast upon hands and feet, with his tongue thrust forth of his mouth, his eyes fierie, vomiting, with store of cold sweats, and lastly, the bloud flowing forth by his eares, nose, mouth, fundament and yard. I gave him eight ounces of oile to drinke, but it did him no good, for it came too late. Wherefore at length hee died with great torment and exclamation, the seventh houre from the time that hee tooke the poison being scarcely passed. I opened his body in the presence of the Jailor and foure others, and I found the botome of his stomacke blacke and dry, as if it had beene burnt with a Cautery; whereby I understood he had sublimate given him; whose force the Spanish Bezahar could not represse, wherefore the King commanded to burne it.

The caustick force of sublimate.

HOW
TO MAKE REPORTS

Now it onely remaines that wee instruct the Chirurgion in making or framing his reporte, or opinion, eyther of the death of any person, or of the weakenesse, or deprivation of any member in the function or execution of its proper office and duty. Herein it is meete that hee be very considerate, that is to say, ingenious or wise in making his report, because the events of diseases are oftentimes doubtfull and uncertaine, neither can any man foretell them certainly, whether they will be for life or death, by reason of the manifold nature of the subject of which we speake, and also the uncertaine condition of the humors both in their kind and motion. Which was the cause why *Hippocrates* even in the first of his Aphorismes pronounceth, that judgement is difficult. But first of all, it is very expedient that a Chirurgion be of an honest mind, that hee may alwayes have before his eyes a carefull regard of true piety, that is to say, the feare of God and faith in Christ, and love toward his neighbours with hope of life everlasting, least that hee being carried away by favour, or corrupted with money or rewards, should affirme or testifie these wounds to bee small that are great, and these great that are small; for the report of the wound is received of the Chirurgion according to the civill Law.

Why a Chirurgion must be carefull in making of Reports.

Why judgement is difficult.

It is recorded in the workes of ancient Physitions that wounds may bee called great for three respects.

The first is by reason of the greatnesse of the dissolved unitie or resolution of Continuity, and such are these wounds which made by a violent stroake with a backe-sword, have cut off the arme, or legge, or overthwart the breast. The second is by reason of the dignitie or worthinesse of the part; now this dignity dependeth on the excellencie of the action; therefore thus any little wound made with a bodkin, knife, in any part whose substance is noble, as in the Braine, Heart, Liver or any other part whose action and function is necessary to preserve life, as in the Weasand,[1] Lungs or Bladder, is judged great. The third is, by reason of the greatnesse and ill habit, or the abundance of ill humors or debility of all the wounded body; so those woundes that are made in nervous parts, and old decayed people, are sayd to be great. But in searching of wounds let the Chirurgion take heede that he be not deceived by his probe. For many times it cannot goe into the bottome of the wound but stoppeth, and sticketh in the way, either because he hath not placed the patient, in the same posture, wherein he was when he received his hurt; or else for that the stroake being made downe right, slipt aside to the right or left hand, or else from below upwards, or from above downewards, and therefore hee may expect that the wound is but little and will be cured in a short time, when it is

like to bee long in curing, or else mortall. Therefore from the first day it behooveth him to suspend his judgement of the wound untill the ninth, for in that time the accidents will shew themselves manifestly, whether they be small or great, according to the condition of the wound, or wounded bodyes, and the state of the ayre according to his primitive qualities, or venomous corruption.

But generally the signes, whereby we may judge of diseases, whether they bee great or small, of long or short continuance, mortall or not mortall, are foure. For they

[1] i.e. œsophagus, or throat.

are drawne either from the nature, and essence of the disease, or from the cause or effects thereof, or else from the similitude, proportion and comparison, of those diseases with the season or present constitution of the times. Therefore if wee are called to the cure of a greene wound, whose nature and danger is no other but a simple solution of Continuity in the musculous flesh, we may presently pronounce that wound to be of no danger, and that it will soone be cured. But if it have an Ulcer annexed unto it, that is, if it be sanious, then we may say it will be more difficult and long in the curing; and so we may pronounce of all diseases, taking a signe of their essence and nature. But of the signes that are taken of the causes, let this bee an example. A wound that is made with a sharpe pointed and heavie weapon, as with an halbeard being stricken with great violence, must be accounted great, yea and also mortall if the accidents be correspondent.

But if the patient fall to the ground through the violence of the stroake, if a cholericke vomiting follow thereon, if his sight faile him, together with a giddinesse, if blood come forth at his eyes and nosthrills, if distraction follow with losse of memory and sense of feeling, we may say; that all the hope of life, remaineth in one small signe which is to be deduced from the effects of the wound. But by the comparing it unto the season that then is, and diseases that then assault mans body, wee may say, that all those that are wounded with gunshot are in danger of death, as it happened in the schirmishes at the seige of *Rouen*, and at the battall of Saint *Denis*. For at that time, whether it were by reason of the fault of the heavens, or ayre, through the evill humors of mans body, and the disturbance of them; all wounds that were made by gunshot, were for the most part mortall. So likewise at certaine seasons of the yeare, we see the small pockes and measels breake forth in children, as it were by a certaine pestilent contagion to the destruction of children onely, inferring a most cruell vomit and laske,[1] and

Wounds deadly by the fault of the ayre.

[1] i.e. lask, or diarrhoea.

in such a season the judgement of those diseases is not difficult. But you by the following signes may know what
parts are wounded. If the patient fall downe with the
stroake, if he lye senselesse, as it were asleepe, if he voyde
his excrements unwittingly, if he be taken with giddinesse,
if blood come out at his eares, mouth, and nose, and if he
vomit choller, you may understand that the scull is fractured, or pearced through, by the defect in his understanding and discourse. You also may know when the scull is
fractured, by the judgement of your externall senses, as if
by feeling it with your finger you finde it elevated or
depressed beyond the naturall limits, if by striking it with
the end of a probe, when the *Pericranium* or nervous filme
that investeth the scull is cut crosse wise; and so divided
there from it, yeeld a base and unperfect sound like unto
a pot sheard that is broken, or rather like unto an earthen
pitcher that hath a cleft, or rent therein.

But we may say, that death is at hand if his reason and
understanding faile him, if he be speechlesse, if his sight
forsake him, if he would tumble headlong out of his bed,
being not at all able to moove the other parts of his body;
if he have a continuall feaver, if his tongue be blacke with
drienesse, if the edges of the wound bee blacke or dry, and
cast forth no sanious matter, if they resemble the colour of
salted flesh, if he have an apoplexie, phrensie, convulsion
or palsie with an involuntarie excretion, or absolute suppression of the Urine and excrements. You may know that

a man hath his throate, that is, his weason and winde pipe
cut. First by the sight of his wound, and next by the
abolishment of the function or office thereof both wayes,
for the patient can neither speake nor swallow any meate
or drinke; and the parts that are cut asunder, divide themselves by retraction upwards or downewards one from

Signes that a
wound hath
pierced in the
capacity of
the chest.

another, whereof commeth sodaine or present death. You
may know that a wound hath peirced into the brest or
concavity, of the body, if the ayre come forth at the wound,
making a certaine whizzing noyse, if the patient breathe

with great difficulty, if he feele a great heavinesse or weight, on or about the midriffe, whereby it may be gathered that a great quantity of blood, lyeth on the place or midriffe, and so causeth him to feele a weight or heavinesse, which by little and little, will bee cast up by vomiting. But a little after a feaver commeth, and the breath is unsavory, and stinking, by reason that the putrefying blood is turned into *sanies*: the patient cannot lye but on his backe, and he hath an often desire to vomit, but if hee escape death, his wound will degenerate into a Fistula, and at length will consume him by little and little.

We may know that the Lungs are wounded, by the foaming and spumous blood, comming out both at the wound and cast up by vomiting; hee is vexed with a greevous shortnesse of breath and with a paine in his sides. *Signes that the Lungs are wounded.*

We may perceive the Heart to be wounded by the aboundance of blood that commeth out at the wound, by the trembling of all the whole body, by the faint and small pulse, palenesse of the face, cold sweate, with often swounding, coldnesse of the extreame parts, and suddaine death. *That the heart is wounded.*

When the midriffe (which the Latines call *Diaphragma*) is wounded, the patient feeleth a great weight in that place, he raveth and talketh idlely, he is troubled with shortnesse of winde, a cough, and fit of greevous paine, and drawing of the entralls upwards. Wherefore when all these accidents appeare, we may certainely pronounce that death is at hand. *The midriffe.*

Death appeareth sodainely, by a wound of the hollow Veine, or the great Arterie, by reason of the great and violent evacuation of blood and spirits, whereby the functions of the Heart and Lungs are stopped and hindred. *The Vena Cava and great Artery.*

The marrow of the backebone being pierced, the patient is assaulted with a Palsie or convulsion very suddainely, and sence and motion faileth in the parts beneath it, the excrements of the bladder, are either evacuated against the patients will, or else are altogether stopped. *The spinall marrow.*

When the Liver is wounded, much blood commeth out *The Liver.*

at the wound, and pricking paine disperseth it selfe even unto the sword-like gristle, which hath its situation at the Lower end of the brest bone called *Sternon*: the blood that falleth from thence downe into the intestines doth oftentimes inferre most maligne accidents, yea and sometimes death.

The
stomacke.
When the stomacke is wounded, the meate and drink come out at the wound; there followeth a vomiting of pure choler, then commeth sweating and coldnesse of the extreame parts, and therefore we ought to prognosticate death to follow such a wound.

The spleene.
When the milt or spleene is wounded, blacke and grosse blood cometh out at the wound, the patient will be very thirsty, with paine on the left side, and the blood breakes forth into the belly, and there putrifying causeth most maligne and greevous accidents and often times death to follow.

The guts.
When the guts are wounded, the whole body is griped and pained, the excrements come out at the wound, whereat also often times the guts breake forth with great violence.

The kid-
neyes.
When the reines or Kidnyes are wounded, the patient will have great paine in making his Urine, and the blood commeth out together therewith, the paine commeth downe even unto the groine, yard, and testicles.

The bladder.
When the bladder and Ureters are wounded, the paine goeth even unto the entralls; the parts all about, and belonging to the groine are distended, the Urine is bloody that is made, and the same also commeth often times out at the wound.

The womb.
When the wombe is wounded, the blood commeth out at the privities, and all other accidents appeare, like as when the bladder is wounded.

The Nerves.
When the sinewes are pricked or cut halfe asunder, there is great paine in the affected place, and there followeth a suddaine inflammation, fluxe, abscesse, feaver, convulsion, and oftentimes a gangreene or mortification of the part, whereof commeth death, unlesse it be speedily prevented.

Having declared the signes and tokens of wounded parts, it now remaineth that we set downe other signes of certaine kindes of death that are not common, or naturall, whereabout, when there is great strife and contention made, it oftentimes is determined and ended by the judgement of the discreete Physition or Chirurgion.

Therefore if it chance that a nurse either through drunkennesse, or negligence, lyes upon her infant lying in bed with her, and so stifles or smothers it to death. If your judgement be required, whether the infant dyed through the default, or negligence of the nurse? or through some violent or suddaine diseases that lay hidden and lurking in the body thereof? You shall finde out the truth of the matter by these signes following. _{Signes that an infant is smothered, or over-layd.}

For if the infant were in good health before, if he were not froward or crying, if his mouth and nosethrills now being dead, be moystned or bedewed with a certaine foame, if his face be not pale but of a Violet or purple colour; if when the body is opened the Lungs be found swolne and puffed up, as it were with a certaine vaporous foame and all the other entralls sound, it is a token that the infant was stifled, smothered or strangled by some outward violence.

If the body or dead corpse of a man be found lying in a field, or house alone, and you be called by a magistrate to deliver your opinion, whether the man were slaine by lightning or some other violent death? you may by the following signes finde out the certainety hereof.

For every body that is blasted, or striken with lightning, doth cast forth or breathe out an unholsome, stinking or sulphureous smell, so that the birdes or fowles of the ayre, nor dogges will not once touch it, much lesse prey or feede on it: the part that was stricken often times sound, and without any wound, but if you search it well, you shall finde the bones under the skinne to be bruised, broken or shivered in peeces. _{Signes of such as are slaine by Lightning.}

But if the lightening hath pierced into the body, which

making a wound therein (according to the judgement of *Pliny*) the wounded part is farre colder than all the rest of the body. For lightning driveth the most thinne and fiery ayre before it, and striketh it into the body with great violence, by the force whereof the heate that was in the part is soone dispersed, wasted and consumed. Lightening doth alwayes leave some impression or signe of some fire either by ustion or blacknesse: for no lightning is without fire.

Moreover whereas all other living creatures when they are striken with lightening fall on the contrary side, onely man falleth on the affected side, if hee be not turned with violence toward the coast or region from whence the lightening came.

If a man bee striken with lightening while he is asleepe, hee will be found with eyes open; contrarywise, if hee be striken while hee is awake, his eyes will be closed (as *Plinie* writeth.) *Philip Commines* writeth that those bodyes that are stricken with lightning are not subject to corruption as others are.

Therefore in ancient time it was their custome neither to burne, nor bury them, for the brimstone which the lightning bringeth with it, was unto them in stead of salt, for that by the drynesse and fiery heate thereof it did preserve them from putrefaction.

Also it may be enquired in judgement, Whether any that is dead and wounded, received these wounds alive or dead. Truely the wounds that are made on a living man, if he dye of them, after his death will appeare red and bloody, with the sides or edges swollne, or pale round about: contrary wise, those that are made in a dead man, will bee neither red, bloody, swollne, nor puffed up. For all the faculties and functions of life in the body doe cease and fall together by death; so that thenceforth no spirits nor blood can be sent, or flow unto the wounded place. Therefore by these signes which shall appeare, it may be declared that hee was wounded dead or alive.

The like question may come in judgement when a man is found hanged, whether he were dead, or alive. Therefore if he were hanged alive, the impression or print of the rope will appeare red, pale, or blacke, and the skinne round about it will be contracted or wrinkled, by reason of the compression which the cord hath made; also often times the head of the *aspera arteria*[1] is rent and torne, and the second spondile, and the necke luxated or mooved out of his place. Also the armes and legges will be pale, by reason of the violent and sodaine suffocation of the spirits: moreover there will be a foame about his mouth, and a foamie and filthy matter hanging out at his nosethrills, being sent thither both by reason that the Lungs are sodainely heated and suffocated, as also by the convulsive concussion of the braine like as it were in the falling sicknesse. Contrariwise, if he be hanged dead, none of these signes appeare: for neither the print of the rope appeares red or pale, but of the same colour as the other parts of the body are, because in dead men the blood and spirits doe not flow to the greeved parts.

Whosoever is found dead in the waters, you shall know whether they were throwne into the water alive or dead. For all the belly of him that was throwne in alive, will be swollen, and puffed up by reason of the water that is contained therein; certaine clammie excrements come out at his mouth and nosethrills, the ends of his fingers will be worne and excoriated, because that hee dyed striving and digging or scraping in the sand or bottome of the river, seeking somewhat whereon hee might take hold to save himselfe from drowning. Contrariwise if he be throwne into the waters being dead before, his belly will not be swollne, because that in a dead man all the passages and conduites of the body doe fall together, and are stopped and closed, and for that a dead man breathes not, there appeareth no foame nor filthy matter about his mouth and nose, and much lesse can the toppes of his fingers be worne and

Signes whether one be hanged alive or dead.

Whether one found dead in the water came therein alive or dead.

[1] i.e. the trachea.

excoriated, for when a man is already dead, he cannot strive against death.

But as concerning the bodies of those that are drowned, those that swimme on the upper part of the water being swollne or puffed up, they are not so by reason of the water that is contained in the belly, but by reason of a certaine vapour, into which a great portion of the humors of the body are converted by the efficacy of the putryfying heate. Therefore this swelling appeareth not in all men which doe perish, or else are cast out dead into the waters, but onely in them which are corrupted with the filthinesse or muddinesse of the water, long time after they were drowned; and are cast on the shore.

Of such as are smothered by Charcoale.

But now I will declare the accidents that come to those that are suffocated and stifled or smoothered with the vapour of kindled or burning charcoales, and how you may foretell the causes thereof by the history following. In the yeere of our Lord God 1575. the tenth day of May, I with *Robert Greauline* Doctor of Physicke, was sent for by Master *Hamell* an advocate of the Court of Parlament of *Paris*, to see and shew my opinion on two of his servants, of whom the one was his Clarke, and the other his Horsekeeper. All his family supposed them dead, because they could not perceive or feele their Arteries to beate, all the extreame parts of their bodyes were cold, they could neither speake nor move, their faces were pale and wanne, neither could they bee raised up with any violent beating or plucking by the haire. Therefore all men accounted them dead, and the question was onely of what kind of death they dyed, for their master suspected that some body had strangled them, others thought that each of them had stopped one anothers winde with their hands: and others judged that they were taken with a sodaine apoplexie. But I presently enquired whether there had beene any fire made with Coales in the house lately, whereunto their master giving eare, sought about all the corners of the chamber (for the chamber was very little and close) and at last found an earthen panne with charcoale halfe burned; which when we once saw, we all affirmed with one voyce, that it was the cause of all this misfortune, and that it was the maligne fume and venemous vapour, which had smothered them, as it were by stopping the passages of their breath. Therefore I put my hand to the regions of their hearts, where I might perceive that there was some life remaining by the heat and pulsation that I felt though it were very little, wherefore we thought it convenient to augment and encrease it. Therefore first of all, artificially opened their mouthes, which were very fast closed, and sticking obstinately together; and thereinto both with a spoone and also with a silver pipe, we put *aqua vitæ* often distilled with dissolved *hiera*[1] and treacle; when we had injected these medicines often into their mouthes, they began to moove and to stretch themselves, and to cast up and expell many viscous excrementall and filthy humors at their mouth and nostrells, and their Lungs seemed to be hot, as it were in their throates.

Therefore then we gave them vomitories of a great quantity of *Oxymel*, and beate them often violently on the last spondill of the backe, and first of the loynes, both with the hand and knee (for unto this place the orifice of the stomacke is turned) that by the power of the vomitory medicine, and concussion of the stomacke, they might be constrained to vomit. Neither did our purpose faile us, for presently they voided clammie, yellow and spumous fleame and blood.

But wee not being content with all this, blowed up into their nostrells out of a Goose quill, the powder of *Euphorbium*, that the expulsive faculty of the braine might be stirred up to the expulsion of that which oppressed it; therefore presently the braine being shaken, or mooved with sneesing and instimulated thereunto by rubbing the chymicall oyle of mints on the pallate and on the cheekes, they expelled much viscous and clammie matter at their nostrells.

[1] ἱερά, a name for many medicines in the Greek Pharmacopœia.

Then we used frictions of their armes, legges, and backe-bones; and ministered sharpe glisters, by whose efficacie the belly being abundantly loosened, they beganne presently to speake and to take things that were ministered unto them of their owne accord, and so came to themselves againe.

In the doing of all these things, *James Guillemeau* Chirurgion unto the King, and of *Paris*, and *John* of Saint *Germanes* the Apothecary, did much helpe and further us.

In the afternoone that the matter being well begunne might have good successe, *John Hautin*, and *Lewis Thibaut*, both most learned Phisitions, were sent for unto us, with whom we might consult on other things that were to be done. They highly commending all things that we had done already, thought it very convenient that cordialls should be ministered unto them, which by ingendering of laudable humors, might not onely generate new spirits, but also attenuate and purifie those that were grosse and cloudy in their bodies. The rest of our consultation was spent in the enquirie of the cause of so dire a mischance. For they sayd that it was no new or strange thing, that men may be smothered with the fume and cloudy vapour of burning coales.

For we reade in the workes of *Fulgosius*, *Volateranus* and *Egnatius*, that as the Emperour *Jovinian*, travelled in winter time toward Rome, he being weary in his journey, rested at a Village called *Dadastanes*, which divideth *Bithynia* from *Galatia*, where he lay in a chamber that was newly made, and plaistered with lime, wherein they burnt many coales, for to dry the worke or plaistering, that was but as yet greene on the walls or roofe of the chamber. Now he dyed the very same night being smothered or strangled with the deadly and poysonous vapour of the burned charcoale, in the midst of the night; this happened to him in the eighth moneth of his reigne, the thirtyeth yeere of his age, and on the twentyeth day of August. But what neede we to exemplifie this matter by the ancient histories, seeing that not many yeeres since three servants dyed in the house of *John Begine* goldsmith, who dwelleth at the turning of the bridge of the Change, by reason of a fire made of coales in a close chamber, without a chimney where they lay. And as concerning the causes, these were alleaged. Many were of opinion that it happened by the default of the vapour proceeding from the burned coales, which being in a place voyd of all ayre or wind, inferres such like accidents as the vapour of muste or new wine doth, that is to say, paine, and giddinesse of the head. For both these kindes of vapour besides that they are crude, like unto those things whereof they come, can also very suddainely obstruct the originall of the Nerves, and so cause a convulsion, by reason of the grossnesse of their substance.

For so *Hippocrates* writing of those accidents that happen by the vapour of new wine, speaketh. If any man being drunken doe suddainely become speechlesse and hath a convulsion, he dyeth unlesse he have a feaver therewithall; or if he recover not his speech againe when his drunkennesse is over. *Sect. 5. Aph. 5.*

Even on the same manner the vapour of the coales assaulting the braine caused them to be speechlesse, unmoveable and voyde of all sense, and had dyed shortly unlesse by ministring and applying warme medicines into the mouth and to the nosethrells, the grossnesse of the vapour had beene attenuated, and the expulsive faculties mooved or provoked to expell all those things that were noysome: and also although at the first sight the Lungs appeared to be greeved more than all the other parts, by reason that they drew the maligne vapour into the body, yet when you consider them well, it will manifestly appeare that they are not greeved, unlesse it be by the simpathy or affinity that they have with the braine when it is very greevously afflicted.

The proofe hereof is, because presently after, there followeth an interception or defect of the voyce, sense and motion: which accidents could not bee unlesse the beginning or originall of the nerves were intercepted or letted from performing its function, being burthened by some matter contrary to nature.

The occasion of the death of such as have the apoplexie. And even as those that have an apoplexie doe not dye but for want of respiration, yet without any offence of the Lungs, even so these two young mens deathes were at hand, by reason that their respiration or breathing was in a manner altogether intercepted, not through any default of the Lungs, but of the braine and nerves distributing sence and motion to the whole body and especially to the instruments of respiration. Others contrariwise contended and sayd, that there was no default in the braine, but conjectured the interception of the vitall spirits letted or hindered from going up unto the braine from the heart, by reason that the passages of the Lungs were stopped, to be the occasion that sufficient matter could not be afforded for to perserve and feed the animall spirit. Which was the cause that those young men were in danger of death, for want of respiration, without the which there can be no life.

For the heart being in such a case, cannot deliver it selfe from the fuliginous vapour that encompasseth it, by reason that the Lungs are obstructed by the grossenesse of the vapour of the coales, whereby inspiration cannot well bee made, for it is made by the compassing ayre drawne into our bodyes: but the ayre that compasseth us doth that which nature endeavoureth to doe by inspiration, for it moderateth the heate of the heart, and therefore it ought to bee endued with foure qualities. The first is, that the quantity that is drawne into the body bee sufficient. The second is, that it be cold, or temperate in quantity. The third is, that it be of a thinne and meane consistence. The fourth is, that it be of a gentle and benigne substance.

Conditions of the ayre good to breath in. But these foure conditions were wanting in the ayre which these two young men drew into their bodyes being in a close chamber.

For first, it was little in quantity, by reason that small quantity that was contained in that little close chamber, was partly consumed by the fire of coales, no otherwise than the ayre that is conteined in a cupping glasse is consumed in a moment by the flame so soone as it is kindled.

Furthermore it was neither cold nor temperate, but as it were enflamed with the burning fire of coales.

Thirdly, it was more grosse in consistence than it should bee by reason of the admixtion of the grosser vapour of the coales: for the nature of the ayre is so that it may bee soone altered, and will very quickly receive the formes and impressions of those substances that are about it.

Lastly, it was noysome and hurtfull in substance, and altogether offensive to the aiery substance of our bodies. For Charcoales are made of greene wood burnt in pits under ground, and then extinguished with their owne fume or smoake, as all Colliers can tell. These were the opinions ot most learned men although they were not altogether agreeable one unto another, yet both of them depended on their proper reasons. For this at least is manifest, that those passages which are common to the breast and braine, were then stopped with the grossenesse of the vapour of the coales: whereby it appeareth that both these parts were in fault, for as much the consent and connexion of them with the other parts of the body is so great, that they cannot long abide sound and perfect without their mutuall helpe by reason of the loving and friendly sympathy and affinitie that is betweene all the parts of the body one with another.

Wherefore the ventricles of the braine, the passages of the lungs and the sleepie Arteries being stopped, the vitall spirit was prohibited from entring into the braine, and consequently the animall spirit retained and kept in, so that it could not come or disperse its selfe through the whole body, whence happened the defect of two of the faculties necessary for life.

It many times happeneth and is a question too frequently handled concerning womens madenheads; whereof the judgement is very difficult. Yet some ancient women and Midwives will bragge that they assuredly know it by

Of the signes of virginitie.

certaine and infallible signes. For (say they) in such as are virgins there is a certaine membrane or parchment-like skin in the necke of the womb, which will hinder the thrusting in of the finger if it be put in any thing deepe, which membraine is broken when first they have carnall copulation, as may afterwards be perceived by the free entrance of the finger. Besides, such as are defloured have the necke of their womb more large and wide; as on the contrary, it is more contracted, straite and narrow in virgins. But how deceitfull and untrue these signes and tokens are, shall appeare by that which followeth; for this membraine is a thing preternaturall, and which is scarce found to be in one of a thousand from the first conformation. Now the necke of the womb will be more open or straite according to the bignesse and age of the party. For all the parts of the body have a certaine mutuall proportion and commensuration in a well made body.

Lib. de error. popul. *Joubertus* hath written, that at *Lectoure* in *Gasconye*, a woman was delivered of a child in the ninth yeare of her age, and that she is yet alive and called *Joane du Perié* being wife to *Videau Beche* the receiver of the amercements of the King of *Navare*: which is a most evident argument, that there are some women more able to accompany with a man at nine yeares old, than many other at fifteene, by reason of the ample capacity of their wombe and the necke thereof; Besides also, this passage is enlarged in many by some accident, as by thrusting their owne fingers more strongly thereinto by reason of some itching, or by the putting up of a Nodule, or Pessarie of the bignesse of a mans yard, for to bring downe the courses. Neither to have milke in their breasts is any certaine signe of lost vir- Aph. 39. sect. 5. ginity; For *Hippocrates* thus writes; But if a woman which is neyther with child, nor hath had one, have milke in her breasts, then her courses have failed her.

Lib. 4. de hist. animal. cap. 20. Moreover, *Aristotle* reports that there be men who have such plenty of milke in their breasts, that it may be sucked or milked out.

Cardan writes, that he saw at *Venice* one *Antony Bussey* some 30. yeares old, who had milke in his breasts in such plenty, as sufficed to suckle a child, so that it did not onely drop, but spring out with violence like a womans milke. Wherefore let Magistrates beware least thus admonished, they too rashly assent to the reports of women. Let Physitions and Chirurgions have a care least they doe too impudently bring magistrates into an errour, which will not redound so much to the judges disgrace, as to theirs.

Lib. 12. *de subtilit.*

But if any desire to know, whether one be poysoned, let him search for the Symptomes and signes in the foregoing and particular treatise of poysons.[1] But that this doctrine of making Reports may be the easier, I thinke it fit, to give presidents, in imitation whereof the young Chirurgion may frame others. The first president shall be of death to ensue; a second of a doubtfull judgement of life and death; the third of an impotency of a member; the fourth of the hurting of many members.

I *A. P.* Chirurgion of *Paris*, this twentieth day of May by the command of the Counsell, entred into the house of *John Brossey*, whom I found lying in bed, wounded on his head, with a wound in his left temple, piercing the bone with a fracture and effracture, or depression of the broken bone, scailes and *meninges* into the substance of the braine, by meanes whereof, his pulse was weake, he was troubled with raving, convulsion, cold sweate, and his appetite was dejected. Whereby may bee gathered that certaine and speedy death is at hand. In witnesse whereof I have signed this Report with my owne hand.

A certificate of death.

By the Coroners command I have visited *Peter Lucey*, whom I found sicke in bed, being wounded with a Halbard on his right thigh. Now the wound is of the bredth of three fingers, and so deepe that it pierces quite through his thigh with the cutting also of a veine and Artery, whence ensued much effusion of blood, which hath exceedingly weakned him, and caused him to swound often; now all his thigh

Another in a doubtfull case.

---

[1] Not reprinted in the present selection.

is swollne, livide, and gives occasion to feare worse symptomes, which is the cause that the health and safety of the
party is to be doubted of.

In the losse   By the Justices command I entred into the house of *James*
of a member. *Bertey*, to visite his owne brother; I found him wounded
in his right hamme, with a wound of some foure fingers
bignesse, with the cutting of the tendons bending the legge,
and of the Veines, Arteries, and Nerves. Wherefore I
affirme that he is in danger of his life, by reason of the
maligne symptomes that usually happen upon such wounds,
such as are great paine, a feaver, inflammation, abscesse,
convulsion, gangreene and the like. Wherefore he stands
in neede of provident and carefull dressing, by benefit
wherof if he escape death, without doubt he will continue
lame, during the remainder of his life, by reason of the
impotency of the wounded part. And this I affirme under
my hand.

Another in   We the Chirurgions of *Paris*, by the command of the
the hurts of   Senate, this twentieth day of March, have visited Master
divers parts. *Lewis Vertoman*, whom wee found hurt with five wounds.
The first inflicted on his head, in the middle of his forehead
bone, to the bignesse of three fingers, and it penetrates even
to the second table, so that we were forced to plucke away
three splinters of the same bone. The other was athwart
his right cheeke, and reacheth from his eare, to the midst
of his nose, wherefore wee stitched it with foure stitches.
The third is on the midst of his belly, of the bignesse of
two fingers, but so deepe that it ascends into the capacity
of the belly, so that we were forced to cut away portion of
the Kall, comming out thereat, to the bignesse of a wallnut,
because having lost its naturall colour, it grew blacke and
putrified. The fourth was upon the backe of his left hand,
the bignesse almost of foure fingers, with the cutting of
the Veines, Arteries Nerves and part of the bones of that
part; whence it is, that he will be lame of that hand, howsoever carefully and diligently healed.

Now because by hurting the spinall marrow, men become lame, sometimes of a legge; it is fit you know that the spinall marrow descends from the braine like a rivelet for the distribution of the Nerves, who might distribute sense and motion to all the parts under the head; wherefore if by hurting the spinall marrow, the patients armes or hands are resolved or numme, or wholy without sense, it is a signe these Nerves are hurt which come forth of the fifth, sixth, seaventh *vertebræ* of the necke. But if the same accidents happen to the thigh, legge or foote with refrigeration, so that the excrements flow unvoluntarily, without the patients knowledge, or else are totally supprest, it is a signe that the sinewes which proceed from the *vertebræ* of the loynes and holy-bone are hurt or in fault; so that the animall faculty bestowing sense and motion upon the whole body, and the benefit of opening and shutting to the sphincter muscle of the bladder and fundament, cannot shew its self in these parts, by which meanes suddaine death happens, especially if there be difficulty of breathing therewith.

Being to make report of a child killed with the mother, have a care that you make a discreete report, whether the childe were perfect in all the parts and members thereof, that the judge may equally punish the author thereof. For he meriteth farre greater punishment, who hath killed a child perfectly shaped and made in all the members; that is, he which hath killed a live childe, than he which hath killed an *Embryon*, that is, a certaine concretion of the spermaticke body. For *Moses* punisheth the former with death, as that he should give life for life, but the other with a pecuniary mulcte. But I judge it fit to exemplifie this report by a president.

A caution in making report of a woman with child being killed.

I *A. P.* by the Judges command visited Mistris *Margaret Ulmary*, whom I found sicke in bed, having a strong feaver upon her, with a convulsion and effluxe of blood out of her wombe, by reason of a wound in her lower belly, below her navill on the right side, penetrating into the capacity of her belly, and the wombe therein; whence it hath come to passe, that she was delivered before her time, of a male childe, perfect in all his members but dead, being killed by the same wound piercing through his scull, into the marrow of the braine. Which in a short time will be the death of the mother also. In testimony whereof I have put my hand and seale.

INDEX

PRINTED IN
GREAT BRITAIN
AT THE
UNIVERSITY PRESS
OXFORD
BY
CHARLES BATEY
PRINTER
TO THE
UNIVERSITY